THE
PRINCE'S
PERSON

THE PRINCE'S PERSON

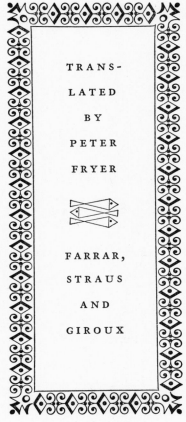

TRANS-
LATED
BY
PETER
FRYER

FARRAR,
STRAUS
AND
GIROUX

ROGER PEYREFITTE

AUTHOR'S NOTE

The details of this story seem very improbable, but they are authentic—I have pieced them together from the original documents. It is certainly the raciest and most scabrous story that has been preserved in the Renaissance archives of Italy.

This portrayal of the morals of extinct noble families cannot shock us. But it does make us wonder at the destiny of a church which has weathered such storms.

R.P.

Part One

1

On March 2, 1581, amid the pealing of Parma's church bells, Vincenzo Gonzaga, son of the Duke of Mantua and Montferrato, and Margherita Farnese, granddaughter of the Duke of Parma and Piacenza, were joined in wedlock. The ceremony took place in the cathedral, under Correggio's fresco depicting the Assumption of the Blessed Virgin. The bridegroom was nineteen, the bride, fourteen; they were the most handsome couple among the Italian nobility.

The festivities went on for a week. By the third day it was being rumoured that the marriage had not been consummated. People looked at the Prince's breeches. They did bulge a good deal—but tailors had been known to pad out codpieces in order to make their wearers appear more dashing than they really were.

When Don Vincenzo's gentlemen in waiting dropped a hint or two, he retaliated with coarse jests. Donna Margherita pretended not to understand what her maids of honour were insinuating. In whom could she confide? Her mother, Maria of Portugal, was dead; her father Alessandro, who governed the Netherlands on behalf of the King of Spain, had not been able to attend the wedding. Her two brothers were younger than she was; though they were pretty precocious, this business would be over their heads. She stood in great awe of her grandfather, Duke Ottavio, and of her grandmother, who was the daughter of Charles v, and upon whom the Pope had conferred the Golden Rose. So she appealed to her great-aunt, the dowager Duchess of Urbino, who lived in Parma and had made something of a pet of her. But the dowager Duchess, though not possessing the Golden Rose, believed that all the works of the flesh, even in married life, were matters of conscience. She therefore interrupted her grandniece and sent her to her brother, Cardinal Farnese, Bishop of Ostia and Velletri, Vice Chancellor of the Holy Roman Church, and Dean of the College of

Cardinals. And to this distinguished confessor the Princess disclosed that—the bird was too big for the nest.

The Cardinal told the Duke, and the Duke sent for the famous Milan physician Acquapendente, who examined Donna Margherita, pronounced her to be normally shaped, and said she would have to get a little older and Don Vincenzo would have to have a little patience.

The Cardinal, however, looked with a suspicious eye on this overamiable bridegroom who had had the impudence to bring to his wedding the Marquis del Vasto, known as 'the Little Marquis.' This young man was the Prince's first cousin and his rather questionable friend. Cardinal Farnese had observed them laughing together, in a far-from-pleasant way, at the portrait of his father, Pier Luigi, the first Duke of Parma and Piacenza and the son of the Farnese pope Paul III. He knew why they laughed, of course. Scandalmongers were secretly keeping alive a story which even Calvin's scurrilous pamphlet against Paul III had ignored, which no historian had dared to publish in any language, and which only a poet, Niccolò Franco, had risked a hint at in his *Priapeia* —thereby deciding Pope Pius v[1] to have him hanged.

On May 27, 1537, Pier Luigi, the Pope's hereditary Gonfalonier, or standard-bearer, while paying a visit to Fano, in the Papal States, had been suddenly inflamed with passion for the Lord Bishop of the town, a handsome young man of twenty-four. His advances were repulsed with horror, so he tied the Bishop up with his own lace rochet and violated him, while two hired toughs, their daggers at the Bishop's throat, prevented the official from shouting for help. This piece of youthful flightiness (as the Pope termed it) had a tragic sequel: the Bishop died, of shame and the pox. The son of this Gonfalonier (and grandson of this Pope) had been made a Cardinal at fourteen and was eighteen when the assault took place; though his own private life was not exactly blameless, he made a point of doing penance for his father on May 27 each year.

Vincenzo Gonzaga might indeed have a weakness for 'the Little Marquis,' Alfonso Fe-

[1] The future Saint.

6

lice d'Avalos di Pescara e del Vasto, and might take a connoisseur's interest in the excesses of his wife's great-grandfather. This did not make him any less of a skirt-chaser; the Mantua ballerinas had initiated him at puberty, and from his seventeenth year he had as his mistress the Countess of Sala, a young and good-looking widow. The Countess owned the magnificent Colorno villa, to which, before his marriage, he would escape for long periods in order to revenge himself on his father, who kept his wings clipped with an allowance of only five hundred crowns a month. Mgr Zibramonte, the ducal counsellor, implored him to think of his salvation; his mother, Leonora of Austria, begged him to behave 'like a Prince of Mantua'; his old tutor, Secretary of State Donati, besought him not to vex his father the Duke; and his intendant, the Marquis of Capilupi, pleaded with to return home, where he ran the risk of finding everything gone—'servants, horses, poultry, timber, and linen.' Meanwhile the Prince went out coursing, acted in private theatricals, and feasted to the music of the Countess of Sala's violins.

Cardinal Farnese knew that the play most

frequently performed at Colorno was *The Squire,* by that lewd writer Aretino. What could be more natural, since it had been written for the court of Mantua, and depicted the morals of that court both recklessly and indulgently: 'a court where women are hated' . . . 'a town full of hermaphrodites'? The part Don Vincenzo liked best was that of the squire himself, an enemy of women, on whom his renowned grandfather had played the trick—so Aretino related—of compelling him to take a wife. But the wife was a page boy in disguise; this was the part the Little Marquis liked best.

The Dean of the College of Cardinals also knew how strangely complaisant the Countess of Sala was towards these young men. All the year round at Colorno they sang the Florentine carnival songs in praise of 'fruits,' as well as the song whose words had been written, long before, by Lorenzo the Magnificent—'The Song of the Men Who Go Backwards':

We go backwards. . .
It's everybody's vice today. . .
Don't be surprised

8

If women do the same
As soon as they come to their senses.

This kind of encouragement had not stopped
Lorenzo's grandnephew Francesco de' Medici,
Grand Duke of Tuscany, from banishing the
Marquis del Vasto for overenthusiasm.

Cardinal Farnese was hardly astonished that
the Duke of Mantua had wanted to marry off
his son as quickly as he could. But why had his
Grace not chosen for him the Grand Duke's
daughter, Leonora, as had at first been con-
templated? Of course, her dowry was only
200,000 crowns, compared with Margherita
Farnese's 300,000. And Don Guglielmo, Don
Vincenzo's father, was not merely stingy, but
positively grasping.

From afar, the Duke took an interest in the
consummation of the marriage, and was told
about the mystery. However much he loved
money, the succession was his first concern. His
two daughters were already settled in life, and
Don Vincenzo was his only son. Over the
cradle, he had taken a vow to build the Basilica
of Santa Barbara, and his wife had taken one to
re-establish the Jesuits in Mantua. He was

afraid that the duchy might pass to his younger brother Ludovico, who had gone off to France to rule his duchy of Nevers and Rethel.

Before Margherita came to Mantua, Don Guglielmo sent Donati to Parma to find out from the Prince himself whether she was penetrable. Rome, replied Don Vincenzo, was not built in a day—not even with Trajan's column.

2

Don Vincenzo set off for his capital to prepare the Princess' reception. A few days later Donna Margherita sailed up the Po on the gilded State barge of the court of Parma, and landed triumphantly on the bank of Vergil's 'smooth-sliding' Mincio. The festivities began again. The Prince was conspicuous, tilting at the quintain and the ring. His dear sister, the third wife of the Duke of Ferrara and Modena, was present, together with their first cousin once removed, Cardinal Gonzaga.

Informed by the Duchess of Mantua—as Cardinal Farnese had been informed by the

Duchess of Urbino—Cardinal Gonzaga tackled Don Vincenzo on the subject of the consummation of his marriage. He got the same reply as the Dean of the College of Cardinals: if the couple had been exerting themselves to no purpose, it was the fault of the wife. The Cardinal lamented the abuse of canon law which had fixed the age of puberty at twelve, and which allowed marriages as premature as certain cardinalships. He himself had received the red hat at thirty-eight, under the present Pope, Gregory XIII, and not at puberty, as had Cardinal Farnese. He assured his cousin that he would help him with prayer, but reminded him of the maxim: 'God helps those who help themselves.'

The wonders of Mantua, multiplied by the Gonzagas' patronage, made the young Princess love her husband all the more. If Parma was proud of its Correggio masterpieces, Mantua boasted those of Mantegna and Giulio Romano. In the Castello San Giorgio, with its big machicolated towers on either side, Donna Margherita gazed upon the frescoes in the Bridal Chamber, which showed her what Don Vincenzo's forebears had looked like and how luxuriously they had lived. The Cupids sur-

rounding the dedicatory inscription to Luido-
vico Gonzaga, 'the unconquerable prince,' and
his wife Barbara, 'the glory of womankind,'
seemed to her to be supporting an inscription
about her own marriage. These Cupids were
no less graceful than she and Don Vincenzo;
but he was the glory of mankind, so broad was
his shaft, and she was an unconquerable
woman, so narrow was her quiver. In the Palazzo del Té, Don Vincenzo proved to her that
he came of good stock: there was a portrait of
his grandfather, under Jove's thunderbolts, half
transformed into a serpent and straining like a
stallion towards the welcoming Olympian
Queen. Other frescoes, with Bacchantes en-
gaged in provoking satyrs whose boldness, and
whose measurements, rivalled those of the
Gonzaga Jupiter, completed the Princess' education. In the Palazzo Ducale, she could ponder over the Gonzaga emblem: a fiery crucible
in which a big bundle of golden rods was being
melted down. Dismissing these images from
her mind, she ended each day kneeling beside
her husband in front of the most sacred relic in
the city and in Christendom: the ampulla of
Most Precious Blood lodged at Mantua by St

Longinus, the soldier who had pierced Christ's side with a spear.

For all his dissolute ways, the Prince was a reverent young man; in this, too, he took after his family. The Blessed Osanna, who was to be seen in a painting trampling the devil under foot, was a Gonzaga on her mother's side; God granted her the birth of the first Duke of Mantua, who was therefore called 'the son of prayer' (and who was portrayed as a phallic dragon in the Palazzo del Té). Don Vincenzo, another 'son of prayer,' must have been moved by this memorial. Francesco Gonzaga[1] was Minister General of the Franciscans and was famed for his saintliness. Another cousin, Luigi,[2] aged fourteen, was preparing himself for the Society of Jesus on the advice of Cardinal Carlo Borromeo,[3] Archbishop of Milan: he was a page at the Spanish court, which he had already perfumed with his virtue, having been brought up at the court of Mantua to keep his eyes and ears shut.

Don Vincenzo loved his wife as much as she loved him. But he was tired of knocking at a

---

[1] The future Venerable. [3] The future Saint.
[2] The future Saint.

13

door that would not open; and so, though he had with some difficulty forced open another door, he set out once more for Colorno. Donna Margherita, of course, had to conceal her jealousy.

Next year they went to Ferrara for the carnival. The Este family had at Ferrara a good many paintings and sculptures calculated to revive the virgin wife's desires and sharpen her regrets. In the Palazzo Schifanoia the triumph of Venus and the sign of Taurus tormented her, as did the triumph of Apollo and his innumerable putti. Don Cesare, the adopted son of the Duke of Ferrara, shared Don Vincenzo's amusements. They made up foursomes in the brothels. The attractions of the Ferrarese women were as highly esteemed as those of the Mantuan boys. A proverb, seemingly horticultural, said: 'Mantua for beans, Ferrara for figs, Bologna for apples.'

A praiseworthy idea occurred to the Prince. He would visit the unfortunate Tasso, who, as his father's guest, had delighted the young Vincenzo. Received with open arms at the Estes' court, the author of *Jerusalem Delivered* was now their prisoner: the Duke, Don Alfonso, had pronounced him mad, so as to put him beyond reach of the romantic love of one of his sisters, and had locked him up in the Hospital of St Anne. Don Vincenzo had the supply of food from the ducal table restored to him, and was thanked in a sonnet:

Illustrious Don Vincenzo, I who am languish-
     ing unto death. . . .

But the poet was languishing less than the Princess; she was heartbroken because, though she had consented to acts which did not re-move her maidenhead, she had not, for all that, been able to hold her husband.

3

As soon as the couple returned, Don Gugli-elmo decided to take drastic measures. His son might have his own reasons for being patient, but the Duke had none. Sick, weakened by ill-ness, crippled with gout and rheumatism, he longed for a grandson.

He questioned his daughter-in-law closely, was informed that the situation was unchanged, and asked her to let the court physician, Master Cavallara, examine her. Cavallara was less optimistic than Acquapendente. She had, he said, an 'arctitude' that could not be cured, save at the peril of her life.

Don Guglielmo took counsel with his wife and Cardinal Gonzaga. In spite of his son's protests and the Princess' tears, he made up his mind to send her back to Parma forthwith. Swear as she might that the Blessed Osanna had appeared to her in a dream and promised her a miracle, the Duke remained adamant. He made no reference to an annulment; but he wanted neither the trouble nor the responsibility of having her cured.

Her younger brother, Ranuccio Farnese, was now in Mantua, and she let him into the secret. He was only fourteen, but he could not restrain himself from upbraiding the Prince. Raking together everything he had heard, he accused him of impotence, sodomy, and adultery, and of agreeing to the dismissal of Donna Margherita in order to dishonour the Farnese family. He even hurled family grievances at him. Had not a Gonzaga plotted the murder at Piacenza of his great-grandfather, Pier Luigi Farnese? Had not Cardinal Gonzaga and Cardinal de' Medici frustrated his uncle's ambition to become pope? It was well known that the Gonzagas had always been his family's enemies—and nobody knew this better than Ranuccio, the future Duke of Parma and Piacenza.

The heir to Mantua and Montferrato was no less quick-tempered, but he did not let himself be carried away. He calmed down his young brother-in-law by swearing that he would take his wife back the moment the Parma doctors had cured her.

Don Guglielmo had sent one of his secretaries, Cesare Cavriani, to Duke Ottavio to inform him of his decision. The message was sugared with fair words about the writer's loyalty—words less sincere than those his son had spoken to Don Ranuccio. Soon afterwards brother and sister returned, willy-nilly, to their duchy. Don Vincenzo escorted them as far as the border; then he sped to Colorno, where more accessible embraces awaited him.

The Duke of Parma did everything he could to increase the accessibility of his granddaughter. Acquapendente was brought back to make an incision. Cavriani hastened to announce the happy news to Don Guglielmo: in a few weeks' time the Princess would be freed from her disability, and Don Vincenzo would be able to perform the duties of a husband. The weeks slipped by in fruitless expectation. It turned out that Acquapendente's knife had done no good whatever; they were now waiting for a surgeon from Venice.

Don Guglielmo was unmoved. Cardinal Gonzaga went to Rome and asked the Pope to annul the marriage, so that Don Vincenzo might remarry. Cardinal Farnese and Don Ottavio were immediately informed; they felt that the Gonzagas had played them false, and heaped reproaches on them. Relations between the two courts became strained. Don Ranuccio, despite Gregory XIII's recent edict against duels, claimed the right to send his brother-in-law a challenge. To the Dean of the College of Cardinals, the attempt at divorce looked like another stratagem to prevent his succeeding the octogenarian pontiff. It was unprecedented for an Italian princess to be divorced, and this flagrant insult, coupled with ridicule, would con-

cern the entire Farnese family. They must fore-
stall the Gonzagas' move with ridicule and in-
sults of their own.

Their ambassadors at foreign courts were
instructed to do their utmost to blacken Don
Vincenzo's name. Special envoys were sent out
for the same purpose. The surgeons' visits were
presented in an unexpected light: their object
was no longer to put right the Princess' arctitude, but to establish that she was intact and her
husband depraved. It was suggested that all she
need do was denounce him to the Inquisition;
but a theologian advised silence about the crimi-
nal assaults, since she had put up with them for
over a year without complaint.

The rumour was put about that there was
fresh evidence in favour of Donna Margherita
—evidence provided by the doctor Master Andrea da Fano. It was pointed out that a practi-
tioner bearing a name that reminded people of a
bishop defiled by a Farnese could not be suspected of sympathy towards the Dukes of
Parma. The blood of Pier Luigi was avenged.

Don Guglielmo behaved in a more dignified
way. He did not carry the dispute into the
forum, but confined himself to putting pres-

sure on the Pope: once he knew that the marriage could not be consummated, he was eager for the divorce to be. The couple had already broken off relations. And yet, in the first two months of their separation, they had exchanged the most affectionate letters. True love had united them; happy memories were uniting them still. But the Prince could not forgive the Princess for revealing their intimacies. In vain did she blame her brother and her confessor for the indiscretion. Besides, while she had no one to console herself with, he had the Countess of Sala.

This was precisely why his parents wanted to remarry him as soon as possible. They were all the more anxious to do so when, in a street brawl in Mantua one night in July 1582, he killed the young Scotsman Lord Robert Crichton, a kinsman of the Stuarts. Though he acted in self-defence, public opinion condemned him: he was known to have been jealous of the young foreigner, whose charm, talents, and successes of all kinds had put his own in the shade. The Duke could not punish his son by pillorying him in the Bonacolsi tower, where criminals were exhibited; nor could he have him tied to the rings under the arches of the Arengario and whipped. He instructed his captain of justice to confirm that the Prince's sword was five fingerbreadths shorter than the Scotsman's. He took care to make these measurements public; but they convinced nobody, and gave rise to indecent jokes.

4

Gregory XIII had an embarrassing choice to make. Cardinal Farnese had reported Crichton's murder to him, but Cardinal Gonzaga had shown him the statement of the captain of justice. Cardinal Farnese declared that the Prince was impotent, Cardinal Gonzaga that he was all too potent. Cardinal Farnese enumerated his catamites, Cardinal Gonzaga his mistresses—adding that, on the night of the brawl, Don Vincenzo had been on his way to a house of ill fame near the Church of St Mark.

Unlike the Prince of Mantua, the sovereign pontiff had provoked no doubts about his own virility. He had begotten a son, Don Giacomo

Buoncompagni, while he was a delegate to the Council of Trent. That venerable assembly had gone on for so long that a number of the Fathers, in their efforts to relieve the tedium, had become fathers in the profane sense, too. Cardinal Farnese had begotten his daughter Clelia; she, together with his palace and his Church of Jesus, were, he said, 'the loveliest things he had made.' He married her, at the age of fifteen, to the Marquis of Civitanuova, thereby shielding her from the unremitting attentions of Cardinal de' Medici.

Gregory XIII and Paul III were not the only popes to have issue. Sixtus IV, Adrian VI, and Clement VII each had a son; Julius II and Julius III each had a daughter; Alexander VI had four children, and Innocent VIII was credited with sixteen, a feat which earned him the title of 'the true father of Rome.' The election of popes whose virility had been publicly proved led to the disappearance of the custom of testing it secretly before they were proclaimed. At all events, Gregory XIII had been the first Pope to legitimate his son. He had had him married in St Peter's, amid great pomp, before the ambassadors and the College of Cardinals; had exhibited in the Vatican the wedding presents sent by all the Christian princes; and had appointed him General of the Holy Roman Church, an office no less important than that of Chief Gonfalonier. It was this beloved son he turned to for advice about the Mantua affair.

His two nephews, Buoncompagni and Vastavillani, whom he had made cardinals at his accession, were divided on the subject; so, in consequence, were their fellow cardinals. Most of these, in fact, were under obligation, either to these two nephews (who had at their disposal the Church's wealth and offices) or to the three whose magnificence surpassed even theirs: Cardinal de' Medici, Senior Deacon and owner of the Medici villa on the Pincio hill; Cardinal d'Este, Archbishop of Auch and Protector of France, and owner of the Este villas on the Quirinal hill and at Tivoli; and Cardinal Farnese; Protector of Naples and Sicily, Portugal, Poland, and Germany, and owner of the Farnese palace. The foreign cardinals who were members of royal families, like the two Archdukes of Austria, attended but rarely; Cardinal de Lorraine de Guise never attended at all.

The disagreement within the College of Cardinals, and between the Pope's two nephews, was only a reflection of the Holy Father's own indecision. Having been elected in a contest with Cardinal Farnese, he had to handle him with kid gloves. During Holy Year he had given hospitality to the Cardinal's brother, Duke Ottavio; to his sister-in-law, Margherita of Austria, he had granted the Golden Rose, in acknowledgment of the services she had rendered to Christianity as Governor of the Netherlands; and he was writing to the Cardinal's son, Prince Alessandro, urging him to send against the Protestants of Germany the Spanish army occupying the Netherlands. In another way, too, the Mantua affair had political implications. Don Vincenzo would inherit a duchy which, united to Montferrato, was one of the keys to Italy and, as such, was a concern of the ecclesiastical State. It was well known that, were his marriage to the Princess of Parma to be annulled, the Prince could again cast his eyes on Princess Leonora de' Medici, the Senior Deacon's niece.

On the day he was elected as arbitrator, Don Giacomo Buoncompagni presented Gregory xiii with two hooded falcons and twelve chamberpots. This was his tribute in return for the two gifts his august father had made him: the marquisate of Vignola, in the Modenese, bought from the Duke of Ferrara for 75,000 crowns, and the duchy of Sora and Arce, in Campania, bought from the Duke of Urbino for 110,000 crowns.

Gregory xiii, seated on a throne ornamented with the papal tiara and the tailless dragon of his coat-of-arms, benignly accepted the two falcons for his aviary and the twelve chamberpots for the papal chamber. Don Giacomo reminded the pontiff that he had promised to confer a cardinalship on his brother-in-law, Captain General Sforza of Santa Fiora, who was only twenty years old, and who was ambitious of exchanging his helmet for a cardinal's hat. The Pope replied, under the seal of secrecy of the Holy Office, that this would be an item on the long list of promotions—the seventh in his ten years' reign—that he was preparing, quietly and at leisure. He was planning to create a score of cardinals; yet he was to disappoint the ambitions of the various crowns. With almost every despatch from

France, Henri III and his mother, Catherine
de' Medici, were recommending candidates—
and not always the same ones. Cardinal Perrenot de Granvelle, Archbishop of Malines,
Cardinal de la Baume, Archbishop of Besançon, and Cardinal Albert of Austria, Viceroy of
Portugal, were importuning him on behalf of
the King of Spain; Cardinal Andrew of Austria, Papal Legate at Cologne, and Cardinal Al-
temps, Bishop of Constance, were harassing
him on behalf of the Emperor. The King of
Poland, Stephen Báthory, had sent his nephew
Andrew, Coadjutor to the Bishop of Ermland,
and Prince Albert Radziwill, Coadjutor to the
Bishop of Vilna, who were dreaming of high
office, although the former was only sixteen,
the latter only twenty-six. Don Giacomo was
fully aware of all this; he was, after all, the
most canvassed individual in Rome.

Honouring the Holy Father by his blameless
conduct and his already numerous progeny,
Don Giacomo was strict about morals. He had
therefore paid more heed to the rumours about
the Prince of Mantua's morals than to those
about his potency. He told the Pope what was
being said about the Prince's scandalous inti-

macy with his cousin the Marquis del Vasto. The Pope replied that it was necessary to avoid rash judgments, but that, when the evidence was irrefutable, he was accustomed to take severe measures without hesitation. Had he not, a few years before, caused seven Spanish sodomites and an Albanian, joined in sacrilegious marriages, to be burned on the Sant' Angelo bridge? Stroking his beard, he added that it was better to leave the Little Marquis alone for the time being. The Papal Chamber was on the point of purchasing from him, for the sum of 40,000 crowns, two fiefs which it would be good for Don Giacomo to have in his hands: the county of Aquino, birthplace of St Thomas, and the seigniory of Arpino, birthplace of Cicero. It had come to the Pope's ears that his daughter-in-law was pregnant, and he wanted to extend the apanages of a son who was renewing for him the joy of being a grandfather.

The imperturbable Don Giacomo asked Gregory XIII if he did not regret having given the Golden Rose to Henri of Anjou, King of Poland, afterwards Henri III, and having sent Don Giacomo himself to Ferrara to greet that monarch on his return from Poland, and having soon thereafter welcomed to Rome his principal catamite, the Duke of Joyeuse, whose brother he had made Archbishop of Narbonne at the age of twenty. The Pope declared that, for the head of the Church, reason of State and the higher interests of the Faith were often identical. He told his son, still under the seal of secrecy of the Holy Office, that he would make the Archbishop of Narbonne a cardinal in his next list of promotions. He went on to say that, in place of creating the other cardinals to which the King of France was laying claim, he had, and would have, still better ways of pleasing him. On this king there rested the hopes for Catholicism in France; he had therefore made him a grant of 200,000 crowns to help him against the Huguenots—and had even sent this sum in a consecrated purse. On the King's request, he was going to fulminate a Bull against French counterfeiters. At the instance of Mgr de Foix, Archbishop of Toulouse and the French King's ambassador in Rome, he was granting him a favour which appeared useless in the case of Vincenzo Gonzaga and Margherita Farnese: a week's special jubilee to make fruitful his marriage with Louise of Lorraine by inducing God to give them 'a handsome Dauphin.' Nevertheless, in communicating this glad news to the King, the Archbishop urged him, in the name of the Pope, to 'take the necessary road' leading to such a result. If the Prince of Mantua was not taking this road, it was a pity. The Church could not forget that he was the great-grandchild of one of its gonfaloniers, as was Margherita Farnese; nor could it forget that Mantua possessed the ampulla of Most Precious Blood.

The General of the Holy Roman Church did not labour the point. He could see, he said, only one way of settling this dispute between the descendants of the two gonfaloniers: to ask a cardinal to make a report and to decide the matter in the Consistory Court. The Pope admired his son's wisdom. He appointed Cardinal Borromeo, the hero of the Milan plague and a nephew of Pius IV. This archbishop was allied to the Gonzagas, but respected by the Farneses. In view of his efforts to extend Lent at the expense of Carnival, the satirists promptly congratulated him on having such a spicy case to investigate on behalf of the Consistory of Unreason.

5

Rome, Italy, the whole of Europe, were now in a fever of excitement over what had quickly become an open secret. People were amused or indignant, according to their temperament. The Spanish court, amid whose ostentation Donna Margherita's father had spent his youth, did not conceal its reprobation. Nor did the Austrian court, nor even the frivolous court of Scotland. There was gloating in the palaces of the heretical princes. Everywhere, people thirsted for the details.

In France, where his Most Christian Majesty was waiting for the result of his special jubilee, inquirers addressed themselves to the prelates of Italian origin, who owed their dioceses to the Queen Mother. Cardinal d'Este was to all intents and purposes an Archbishop *in partibus,* but the others were compelled to be resident: the Bishop of Albi, Mgr Julian de' Medici; the Bishop of Paris, Mgr de Gondi; the Bishop of Angoulême, Mgr de Boni; the

Bishop of Béziers, Mgr de Bonzi; the Bishop of Saint Papoul, Mgr de Bardis. All these were Florentines; there was also a Roman, the Archbishop of Arles, Mgr de Santacroce.

This tide of curiosity did not escape the Pope's notice; but it did not disturb him. On the contrary, it strengthened his resolve to provide a shining example of the Church's serenity in the face of such a delicate problem. And this was the subject of his conversations with the cardinals and the ambassadors, whose opinions he was pretending to collect. The most serious and urgent questions were left in abeyance.

Gregory XIII neglected the plan for a raid on England, for which the Nuncio in Paris, Mgr Castelli, was paying 4,000 crowns to the Duke of Guise; the plan to assassinate Queen Elizabeth, which Mgr Sega, the Nuncio in Madrid, was fomenting; and the petition from the Catholic nobles in England asking for a dispensation to commit this assassination. Queen Elizabeth, excommunicated by Pius V, of blessed memory, was now of interest to his successor only because, like the Princess of Mantua, she was suffering from incurable virginity.

Gregory XIII neglected the disorderliness in the electorate of Cologne, where the ex-Archbishop, Gebhart Truchses, was marrying the Canoness Agnès de Mansfeld—just as, in the time of Pius IV, Cardinal de Coligny had married his concubine, Isabelle de Loré.

Gregory XIII neglected the massacre of St Bartholomew, which had enlivened the start of his pontificate, and which the Nuncio Salviati had instigated under Pius V, of blessed memory. He forgot the Te Deum that he had caused to be sung in the Basilica of St Mark, the mass he had caused to be celebrated in the church of Santa Maria Sopra Minerva, the commemorative medal he had caused to be struck, the frescoes he had caused to be painted in the Royal Hall of the Vatican, the Bull in which he had decreed a universal jubilee, the consecrated cap and tuck that he had bestowed on Charles IX.

Gregory XIII forgot the ex-Dominican heresiarch Jacques Paléologue, whom the German princes had handed over to him (after refusing to perform that service for Pius V), and who was in the prison of the Inquisition, awaiting trial.

Gregory XIII forgot his sorrow at not having crowned Maximilian II and Rudolph II as Kings of the Romans, Kings of the Lombards, and Emperors, as he had seen Charles V crowned in Bologna by the Medici Pope Clement VII (whom the Emperor afterwards aided and abetted).

Gregory XIII forgot the King of Poland, whose armies were frightening the Great Muscovite to the point where he was begging the Pope to mediate. Ivan's ambassador, Molvianinov, had been received in the Mappamundi Hall of the Palace of St Mark, had presented the Pope with sables, hesitated a long time before kissing his foot, felled a hidden chamberlain with his fist, and gone back with a Golden Bull blessing Russia and a picture of the Saviour for the Great Muscovite.

Gregory XIII forgot his œcumenical dreams, which flattered the Jesuits of Japan with the homage of three petty Catholic kings, the Jesuits of Goa with the hope of converting the Great Mogul, the Jesuit Possevino with the baptism of a northern prince, the Jesuit Saffo with intrigues concerning the Great Sudan, and the Jesuit Abel with promises of high posi-

33

tions and allowances for the patriarchs of the Orthodox Church.

Gregory XIII forgot to busy himself with the implementation of his Bull concerning the 'Jewish scourge,' which he had brought to the attention of the inquisitors the year before. Yet what crimes had he not already laid at the door of these enemies of Christ? They had called up demons and sacrificed to them, taught 'beastly things' to Christians, and forced Christian wet-nurses to express their milk into latrines after Holy Communion.

Gregory XIII forgot that the Roman State was overrun with bandits, including the Duke of Montemarciano, who was the guest of Cardinal de' Medici on the Pincio hill; as the great-great-grandnephew of Pius II and Pius III, he profited by an indult.

Gregory XIII forgot the two friars, dear to his heart and to the people of Rome: Filippo Néri,[1] founder of the Oratory, who had miraculously restored to health one of his old friends, and the Capuchin Felix de Cantalice,[2] who, by making the sign of the cross, multi-

[1] The future Saint.   [2] The future Saint.

plied oil, wine, and wheat in the houses of the poor.

Gregory XIII forgot the triumph of the eleventh Holy Year, which had brought in 119, 466 pilgrims, to whom 305 boxes of Agnus Dei had been distributed, and who had filled his coffers with angels and angelots, saluts and seraphs, doubloons and florins, crown pieces and ducats.

Gregory XIII even forgot the things that would perpetuate his name: the establishment of the Gregorian calendar, and the building of the Gregorian chapels in St Peter's, the Roman, German, and Armenian colleges, the Greek and Slavonian seminaries, the Quirinal palace, the Belvedere gallery, the public granary, and the papal distillery.

Finally, Gregory XIII forgot, once again, what he had been forgetting for ten years: to decree a canonization.

6

On April 11, 1583, the sovereign pontiff said mass at St Mary the Greater, the church assigned for that day's Lenten address. Twenty-eight cardinals supported him. He spoke a few words to them, and to the congregation who were 'gathered together under the mantle of the Virgin to ask that their sins be healed by the balm of her grace.' Then, mounting the white palfrey that he still rode despite his eighty-one years, he returned to the Vatican. He was at the head of the procession, behind the pontifical cross. Since it was Lent, the housings of the cardinals' mules were purple, as were the hoods of their copes. Don Giacomo Buoncompagni, his staff of office in his hand, rode at the rear of the cavalcade: this being a time of penance, there were pearl buttons instead of the usual diamond buttons on his cloak.

The Pope withdrew with his son and his nephews, while herb broth, milk of almonds, stewed pears, and pine-cone kernels were served to the cardinals in the Hall of the Parrots. Since it was Lent, there were only tin fingerbowls, not silver ones. After taking these refreshments, the members of the College put back on their heads their purple hoods and their red hats and made their way to the Royal

Hall. They were going to the secret Consistory to which they had been summoned the previous day by the pontifical messengers. The choice of date had astonished Mgr Mongeat, the chief messenger, a Frenchman by birth. Still more had it astonished Mgr Mucanzio, the Pope's majordomo. Never before, in the recollection of the chief messenger and the majordomo, had a consistory, secret or public, been held in Holy Week. But the Pope had desired to take advantage, without further delay, of the presence of many cardinals, Italian and foreign, who had come to the Eternal City to earn the indulgences of Holy Week.

April 11 was the feast day of St Leo the Great, pope, confessor, and scholar. This made it all the more extraordinary for a meeting to take place whose principal subject matter seemed to offend modesty. St Leo, in fact, had set a memorable example of that virtue: while on the throne of St Peter he had cut off his own hand to punish it for a carnal gesture provoked by a good-looking woman who had kissed it. From that moment the privilege of kissing the sovereign pontiff's hand was limited to bishops and cardinals—even when they were tender adolescents—and the faithful were permitted to kiss only his feet. Lastly, some sticklers for propriety felt it out of place to hear a case of impotence before frescoes depicting the Canossa reconciliation, the taking of Tunis, the battle of Lepanto, and the massacre of St Bartholomew.

Wearing the camauro and the gold embroidered consistorial mitre, the Pope arrived flanked by the Senior Deacon, Cardinal de' Medici, and the Second Deacon, Cardinal Vastavillani, who were holding up the hem of his red pluvial. He mounted the dais on which stood his canopied throne. Mgr Vicentini, hereditary officiator of the *extra omnes,* pronounced those ritual words. The prelates who had escorted the Pope went out, together with the cardinals' train bearers and the General of the Church. There remained only the two clerks, or national secretaries, Mgr Antoniani for the Italian nation and Mgr Strauss for the transalpine nations. They had to take a record of the debates, under the seal of secrecy of the Holy Office, and to draft the decrees. The door would remain shut until Cardinal Commendoni, Cardinal Camerlengo, rang a bell from inside the hall.

After prayers and the invocation of the Holy Ghost, Gregory XIII, now wearing only the camauro on his head, opened the meeting. The cardinals kept on their hoods and their hats. They read the agenda papers, written in Latin, which the messengers had distributed to them. There was first the list of vacant bishoprics—Foligno in the Papal States, Stagno in Dalmatia, Almira and Jacca in Spain, Castres and Lisieux in France—with the names of the candidates.

Quid vobis videtur?—'What is your opinion?'—asked the Pope. All the cardinals stood up and took off their hats, as a sign of approval. Not one of the elections was contested. The decrees were quickly drawn up by the two clerks and read immediately by the Pope.

The next item on the consistorial agenda paper was *De natura principis Mantuae*—'Concerning the nature of the Prince of Mantua.' In curialistic parlance, the word 'nature' referred to the Prince's person as well as his condition. The Pope's 'What is your opinion?' would thus refer to something very different from the pre-

conization of the Franciscan Barzellini as
Bishop of Foligno, the Benedictine Givry des
Cars as Bishop of Lisieux, and Jean de Fossé as
Bishop of Castres. It was the first time that
such an affair had come before the Consistory Court since the days of Benedict XII,
when Margaret of Carinthia, nicknamed 'Big-
mouth,' had secured the annulment of her
marriage to John of Bohemia, Count of the
Tyrol, nicknamed 'the Impotent.' The nephew
cardinals had had no need to impress the importance of this question on their 'brothers in
the purple.' If they decided against the Prince
of Mantua they would be prohibiting him from
remarrying, and would be putting his two
duchies up for auction. They would be giving
permission to the Princess of Parma to remarry, perhaps more brilliantly—the Duke of
Savoy had already sought her hand. They
would be forcing the Duke of Mantua to give
her back her dowry, while forfeiting the 'counterdowry' that he had settled on her, according
to custom. And they would be gambling on the
outcome of the future Conclave, which would
affect the majority of the cardinals as well as
their Dean.

Cardinal Borromeo stood up and bared his head to read his report. He had chosen for an epigraph his double motto: the word *Humilitas* (which his family symbolized by a golden crown) and this pious little prayer, which he now applied to Don Vincenzo: 'Lord, hear my case.'

The marriage, he said, had taken place two years and forty days before—taking account of the change, in the preceding year, from the Julian to the Gregorian calendar—but had not yet been consummated. Some said that the Prince's person was 'wretched and shrunken,' others that it was 'monstrously huge.' According to the Prince's supporters, the Princess was suffering from over-arctitude or from a kind of distortion. The Cardinal had seen Donna Margherita several times in Parma, but her replies were contradictory, as were those of the surgeons. In Mantua and Ferrara, he had questioned Don Vincenzo, who, like the man of gentle birth he was, had refused to reproach his wife and had limited himself to affirming his virility. Nevertheless, a Mantuan ballerina and a male dancer from Modena accused him of impotence. It was said that he had suffered the same insult from the Scotsman, Lord Robert Crichton, who had died at his hands. Moreover, he was not known to have fathered a single bastard, and his liaison with a Colorno widow shed no light on the matter. In short, there was no proof one way or another, and the only positive piece of evidence was this unconsummated marriage. The Cardinal-Archbishop of Milan sat down and replaced his hat on his head.

Quid vobis videtur? asked Gregory XIII.

Cardinal Farnese, who had come to the Royal Hall by carriage in spite of an attack of gout, stood up, bared his head, and begged leave to remain seated while he spoke. They expected a diatribe from him, on the lines of the rumours he had been responsible for; to everyone's surprise, his tone was quite different. He recalled that, in order to establish impotence in an unconsummated marriage, the Church required a period of three years to have elapsed, or alternatively the testimony of seven witnesses of good character—not ballet dancers, male or female. Donna Margherita had a year left, all but fifty days—taking account of the Gregorian calendar.

The Dean and Vice Chancellor had been admirably adroit. He was trying to disconcert the Gonzagas by riveting Don Vincenzo to his chain, believing, of course, that if his wife went back to Mantua she would never leave again. It would not be the only example of a princely marriage remaining childless.

Quid vobis videtur? asked Gregory XIII.

Cardinal Gonzaga, standing and bareheaded, inquired whether the Princess' family would accept the testimony of seven witnesses of good character if they were His Holiness's own surgeons and physicians. This, for the Farneses, was where the shoe pinched; since obtaining Master Andrea da Fano's certificate, they had not permitted any medical man to examine Donna Margherita. Cardinal Farnese replied that the physicians and surgeons had ended their work; and, besides, this testimony of seven witnesses was shameful for women in general and particularly so for a woman of his niece's rank. A woman's modesty was more precious than rubies.

Cardinal Borromeo shared this view. He read a passage from *The Duties of the Clergy,* by his predecessor St Ambrose, holding that the test by examination, inflicted on a virgin, was 'faulty and uncertain, for if the parts that are touched have been opened by chance, modesty is violated; if they have been opened deliberately, the immodesty is bestial.'

Cardinal d'Angennes de Rambouillet, Bishop of Mans, related the case of two Paris damsels who, in 1560, sheltered some Calvinists and were accused of appeasing the lust of these heretics. They obtained from the High Court the right to be examined to prove they were virgins.

Gregory XIII submitted to the cardinals the question of an examination.

Quid vobis videtur? he said.

Cardinals Gonzaga, d'Este, and de' Medici, Cardinal Cesi, Legate at Bologna, and the two French cardinals, Pellevé and d'Angennes de Rambouillet, were the only ones who stood and took off their hats in favour of the testimony by seven witnesses.

There was a majority against the examination of the Princess. In spite of the strictness of the Consistory, Cardinal Farnese cast a grateful glance at his colleagues. He half rose, and said it followed from this decision that they must order the Prince and Princess to live together again. Pope Clement III had enjoined a husband and wife to do so, although the husband had still not carried out his conjugal duty after five years. Pope Alexander III, while permitting a wronged wife to remarry, expressed the hope that the couple might prefer to live together 'like brother and sister.'

Cardinal Gonzaga objected that there was a distinction between the duties of private individuals and those of princely families. The latter were obliged, for the sake of peace in Europe and the happiness of their peoples, to make sure of their succession. Cardinal Farnese observed that this obligation had not weighed with the Head of the Church, gloriously reigning. When their late colleague, Cardinal Braganza, had become King of Portugal, he had been granted a dispensation to renounce the purple—but not one to get married. The cardinals, and even the Holy Father himself, smiled when Cardinal Gonzaga suggested that this dispensation had perhaps been denied to Cardinal Braganza because he was seventy-seven years old.

Cardinal Farnese turned the argument of the

succession against his opponent. He observed that Gregory XIII was preparing to proclaim double rites for the feast day of St Anne, in honour of belated fertility; that St Nicholas of Tolentino and St Giuliana Falconieri were both brought into the world, like the Blessed Virgin Mary, by mothers of an advanced age; that God, in the Old Testament, had granted a son to Abraham and Sarah when they were centenarians.

Cardinal Gonzaga replied that his nephew could not be expected to have the virtues of a partiarch, and that there was a limit to everything.

The Dean and Vice Chancellor asked Cardinal de' Medici and the French cardinals whether the French Queen, Catherine de' Medici, had not been barren for a decade before having ten children in thirteen years. The three cardinals stood up and took off their hats.

Cardinal Farnese said there was a speedy way of providing for the succession—adopting a next of kin. He asked Cardinal d'Este whether his brother, the Duke of Ferrara, after two childless marriages each dissolved by the death of the wife, had not adopted a cousin,

Don Cesare, instead of waiting for a son by Margherita Gonzaga. Cardinal d'Este stood up and took off his hat.

Cardinal Gonzaga declared that, in this case as in that of Queen Catherine de' Medici, the marriage had been consummated immediately, which achieved one of its purposes, a relief of concupiscence. But to keep together a young couple incapable of achieving its other purpose, generation, was to profane the marriage tie, favour adultery, and encourage licentiousness.

Cardinal Deza, president of the kingdom of Granada, recalled that, for the same reason, religious law forbade the marriage of eunuchs. In Spain, however, where eunuchs were numerous, they did get married, thanks to the complaisance of the clergy. He accordingly asked for a Bull emphasizing this prohibition.

Cardinal Quiroga, Archbishop of Toldeo and Grand Inquisitor of Castile, said that such a Bull would be ineffective unless married eunuchs and their wives were excommunicated.

Gregory XIII intervened at this point. Having freed bullfighters from the excommunication imposed by Pius V, of blessed memory, he deemed it prudent not to fulminate against the marriage of eunuchs.

Cardinal Farnese made another effort to get up, and took off his hat as a sign of approval. Since the Spanish cardinals were his regular supporters, and his brother, the Duke of Parma, was Charles v's son-in-law, it was surprising that he should offend them. It was understood however that he did not wish to run the risk of seeing his niece excommunicated, should Don Vincenzo turn out to be a eunuch.

Cardinal Paleotti, Archbishop of Bologna, whose former parish church had been that of St Achilleus and St Nereus, pointed out that those two glorious martyrs, baptized by St Peter, had been eunuchs.

Cardinal Borromeo thought it as well to recall, in support of what Cardinal Gonzaga had said, that according to St Thomas Aquinas, a marriage was null and void if the carnal act could not be accomplished. Cardinal Farnese countered with the different theory of Fr Bellarmine,[1] who held that consummation is an integral, but not an essential, part of marriage. Adam and Eve, this learned Jesuit had said, did

[1] The future Saint.

not know each other until after they were turned out of their earthly paradise; and yet they were already married. Again, the Holy Virgin and St Joseph were married, and yet they remained chaste.

Cardinal Gonzaga retorted that the Holy See had agreed to the separation of princes and princesses when their marriages were childless, whatever the reason. In this way the marriage of David I, King of Neustria, and his wife Comertrude was dissolved, as was that of Louis XII, King of France, and his wife Jeanne.[2]

Cardinal d'Angennes de Rambouillet said that Jeanne of France, who had died in the odour of sanctity, had never accused her husband of impotence; that was the contrary of the present case. Cardinal Sirleto, librarian of the Holy Roman Church, added that the cases of Margaret, Queen of Scotland, and Comertrude, Queen of Neustria, had both been concerned with the barrenness of the wife. Cardinal Borromeo said the Princess of Mantua was not accused of barrenness, since she was a virgin, but of an arctitude or distortion. Cardinal Farnese declared that these arguments had been demol-

---

[2] The future Saint.

ished by Master Andrea da Fano. Cardinal Rusticucci, a Fano nobleman and the permanent administrator of Sinigaglia, said the Fano surgeon enjoyed a deservedly high reputation.

Cardinal Andrew of Austria, Bishop of Brescia, asked whether Margherita Farnese had fulfilled all the duties of a wife, as defined, in honour of Margaret of Carinthia, by the Consistory which, 242 years before, had proclaimed the Count of the Tyrol's impotence. Had she 'consented to and shown herself ready for copulation'? Had she let Vincenzo Gonzaga 'try to know her by all or nearly all possible means'— *omnibus aut quasi omnibus modis?*

Cardinal Farnese replied that Donna Margherita had neglected nothing which was permitted to a self-respecting princess of her age.

The Neapolitan Cardinal d'Avalos d'Aragona, former Chancellor of the kingdom of Naples, former Archbishop of Turin, and cousin of the Little Marquis, put forward the hypothesis that a magic spell had knotted up the husband's lace or narrowed the wife's vessel.

Cardinal Pellevé, Archbishop of Sens, said that magic spells for knotting laces or narrowing vessels were becoming less and less frequent in France, for the Officiality was getting somewhat restive about them. Cardinal de la Baume, Archbishop of Besançon, said the same thing about Franche-Comté. Cardinal d'Avalos d'Aragona cited the Beda penitential, which showed how easy it was, with the help of the Prince of Darkness, not merely to knot a lace, but to stop a horse's gallop, arrest the sails of a windmill, and jam the wheel lock of an arquebus. This penitential threw no light, however, upon the narrowing of vessels.

Cardinal Bonelli, a Dominican and the nephew of Pius v, of blessed memory, quoted the missal of his order, which contained a prayer 'for those impeded *in matrimonio* by demons or evil spells.' Cardinal Quiroga adduced the example of Pedro the Cruel, King of Castile, who had not been able to consummate his marriage with Blanche of Bourbon, his wife, in consequence of a spell cast by his mistress, Maria Padilla.

Cardinal de Santacroce, whose nephew had succeeded him as Archbishop of Arles, and who had introduced tobacco into Italy—thanks to him, it was called 'the holy weed'—drew attention to the fact that there were some deadly spells cast by means of fumigations.

Cardinal Colonna, Legate in La Marche and great-grandnephew of Martin v, asked whether the Prince and Princess of Mantua had complied with the rules in force in cases of impotence and barrenness caused by evil spells: had they 'confessed all their sins, shed tears, mortified the flesh, asked for exorcisms, and distributed alms'?

Cardinal Borromeo replied that exorcisms had not been thought necessary, since the existence of evil spells had not been established.

Cardinal Riario, great-grandnephew of Sixtus iv, asked whether the master surgeon had signed a certificate about the person of the Prince of Mantua.

Cardinal Carafa, grandnephew and former cupbearer of Paul iv, dismissed by Pius iv and recalled by Pius v, expressed his amazement at this interminable discussion about a subject unworthy of the majesty of the College of Cardinals. He begged the Fathers in the purple to become chosen vessels once more, vessels of mercy and purity, and not to busy themselves with other vessels.

Cardinal Gonzaga retorted that the presence of the Head of the Church was enough to remove any suspicion of unworthiness. He quoted St Paul: 'Unto the pure, all things are pure.'

Cardinal d'Angennes de Rambouillet provided an example of the curiosity of the faithful about this kind of case. Catherine de Soubise had brought an action for impotence against Baron de Pont; the latter was one of the deserved victims of the St Bartholomew massacre, and his naked body was thrown under the windows of the Louvre; the King, the Queen, and the court inspected the corpse.

Cardinal Galli, Secretary of State, requested the Sacred College not to stray from the point. He brought the meeting back to Cardinal Borromeo's question: had they or had they not any proof, outside his marriage, of the virility or impotence of the Prince of Mantua?

Cardinal Peretti de Montalto,[3] a conventual Minorite and a former inquisitor—as a boy he had been a shepherd, and used to castrate lambs with his teeth—summed up the debate by setting forth the three canonical conditions

[3] The future Sixtus v.

for virility: *erectio, introductio,* and *emissio.*
How did Don Vincenzo stand?

Quid vobis videtur? asked Gregory XIII.

Cardinal Savelli, Bishop of Oporto and San
Rufino, Vicar of Rome, and great-grandnephew of Honorius III and Honorius IV, said
that the sin of Onan and the sin against nature
were causes of relative, not absolute, impotence.
Cardinal Gonzaga trembled at this allusion to
his nephew's tastes, but he knew Cardinal Farnese also wanted to hide the shameful secrets
that Cardinal Borromeo's modesty had succeeded in veiling. The angel of Sodom flew
away.

Cardinal Caetani, Boniface VIII's great-
grandnephew, who had received the purple at
the age of twelve, said there was temporary impotence and there was permanent impotence.
Cardinal Gonzaga insisted that his nephew was
free from any kind of impotence, even relative
or temporary.

Cardinal Delfino, a patrician from Venice
and formerly Nuncio to the Diet of Nurem-
berg, added that there was also impotence with
virgins—*impotentia in virginem.*

Cardinal d'Este said that he felt obliged—not

without hesitation, but in good faith—to reveal what he had heard from his cousin, Don Cesare d'Este, the adopted son of the Duke of Ferrara and a friend of the Prince of Mantua. The two young men had been in debauches together, and Don Cesare had seen Don Vincenzo fulfil to perfection the three canonical conditions.

Cardinal Cesi said that he felt obliged—not without hesitation, but in good faith—to reveal what he had heard from the Bolognese physician Master Beato: this discreet man had treated a son of the Countess of Mirandola for the French disease, contracted from a woman deflowered by the Prince of Mantua. Here was another proof that the latter could fulfil the three canonical conditions.

Cardinal Gonzaga hastened to declare that, on the pledged word of Don Vincenzo's old tutor, the Secretary of State and physician Donati, the Prince had been cured of the French disease in forty days with the juice of the date plum, *Diospyros lotus*. He thanked Cardinals d'Este and Cesi for having demonstrated, in such an unchallengeable way, the Prince's virility, even *in virginem*.

In his capacity of rapporteur, Cardinal Borromeo said these two testimonies had enlightened him somewhat; he was convinced of the Prince of Mantua's virility.

Quid vobis videtur? asked Gregory XIII.

Nineteen cardinals stood up and took off their hats. The three Neapolitans, d'Avalos d'Aragona, Carafa, and Gesualdo, the Flemish Perrenot de Granvelle, La Baume from Franche-Comté, the two Spaniards, Quiroga and Deza, Cardinal Caetani, who had been appointed by Paul III, and the Dean and Vice Chancellor—these remained seated with their hats on. The second nephew cardinal, Vastavillani, so recently a supporter of Donna Margherita, had gone over to the majority, as had the two Austrian cardinals, who were closer relatives of the Gonzagas, the Estes, and the Medicis than they were of the Farneses.

In a low voice, the Pope gave his instructions to the secretary, who received them impassively, and to the Dean and Vice Chancellor, who fainted. Cardinal Borromeo alone transmitted them to the two clerks, who drew up the decrees while Cardinal Farnese, his eyes shut and his chin on his chest, chanted with his colleagues.

Cardinal de' Medici put the consistorial mitre on Gregory XIII's head. All the cardinals rose and took off their hats. The Pope read solemnly:

'In the name of the Father, and of the Son, and of the Holy Ghost. Amen. Having heard, in Our Apostolic Palace beside St Peter's, the advice of Our beloved brothers, the cardinals of the Holy Roman Church, on the person of Our beloved son, the noble Prince of Mantua, We declare, decree, and profess that there is no ground for doubting his virility; that the non-consummation of his marriage cannot be blamed on him; that it is essential for the peace of Europe and the happiness of its peoples to ensure that his family, which is prolific in pious men and great servants of the Church, has a succession; that the welfare and interests of his wife, Our beloved daughter, the noble Princess of Parma, are as dear to Us as the family to which she belongs, which is prolific in pious men and great servants of the Church, and which is renowned, indeed, for a distinguished servant of the servants of God; that it would be dangerous to recommend that she live with her husband like a sister; that, out of regard for her and her family, We set aside the idea of severing, against her will, the sacred bonds of marriage; but that, if she were to take a vow that she preferred the sublime joys of the cloister to the vain tumult of the world, her marriage would be *ipso facto* null and cancelled, which would permit Our beloved son, the noble Prince of Mantua, to remarry.'

7

It was a heavy blow for the Farneses. The Dean could see no remedy: it was hard to run counter to a resolution that tended to obtain a new bride for Jesus Christ. The Pope had instructed Cardinal Borromeo to try his powers of persuasion on the young woman concerned.

However, this girl whom Love had brushed with his wing tips had no intention whatever, at sixteen, of renouncing the vain tumult of the world. She had never made the slightest vow to enter religion; Don Vincenzo's caresses and the frescoes at Mantua and Ferrara had scarcely prepared her to do so. Her resistance was strengthened by her brother Ranuccio, more enraged than ever at the Gonzagas, and by her grandfather, Duke Ottavio, who was anxious to avoid the shame of her being repudiated by her husband. But her grandmother and her aunt, the Duchess of Urbino, were Cardinal Borromeo's allies in his efforts to lead her to the cloister.

The Archbishop of Milan, with the help of St Paul, showed her how much better off virgins were than wives and widows. Her aunt confirmed this as a widow; her grandmother, as a wife. When Donna Margherita exclaimed that she would prefer being a widow to being a virgin, her catechist pointed out that, in any case, the Apostle of the Gentiles condemned marriage. St Jerome had symbolized the perfection of virginity by the figure 100, widows having 60 and wives only 30. The Archbishop commented on St Ambrose's treatise *Concerning Virginity*. He referred to the celebrated virgins whom the Church venerated, but began inopportunely with St Barbara. This name, dear to the Mantuans, made Donna Margherita sigh: it did not incline her to the cult of virginity.

The Cardinal tried a different way of instilling into her the spirit of the Consistory. He praised the martyred virgins commemorated by the names of the cardinals' churches in Rome: his own, St Prassede; Cardinal Galli's, Sant' Agata in Suburra; St Anastasia for Cardinal Delfino; St Cecilia for Cardinal Gesualdo; St Pudenziana for Cardinal de la Baume; St Lucia for Cardinal d'Avalos d'Aragona; St Euphemia for Cardinal d'Angennes de Rambouillet; St Balbina for Cardinal Quiroga; St Rufina for Cardinal Savelli; and St Susanna for Cardinal Rusticucci. He did not forget St Agnes, although her church was vacant. But he said no more about St Barbara, whose church Cardinal Cesi had had, before transferring to St Vitale's. Donna Margherita confessed that her martyrdom was to be a virgin and no longer chaste.

Then Cardinal Borromeo extolled the princesses who had embraced the religious life of their own accord, as if no prince had been worthy of their hearts. The list was a long one, but the Archbishop felt bound to emphasize an example from his own See. Under his guidance, the eldest daughter of the General of the Church, Scholastica Buoncompagni, brought up by the Benedictine nuns of St Paul in Milan, had taken a vow to remain with them. Donna Margherita, whose husband had given her some lessons in genealogy, shocked the pious Borromeo by replying that this girl was Gregory XIII's granddaughter, while she herself was only the great-granddaughter of Paul III.

To bring her mind back to ideas suitable for her age, the Cardinal recalled the unicorn's horn which, according to St Gregory the Great, could be grasped only by a virgin, and the wolf domesticated by St Austreberta, the Abbess of Pavilly. But Donna Margherita had other ideas about the unicorn's horn and the domestication of the wolf.

Her aunt, to whom she unbosomed herself most freely, eventually told her that when one was not built so as to satisfy a man's appetite, one must curb one's own. This wise remark was more effective than the Archbishop's sermons.

In compensation, the Princess had just found an unexpected ally outside her family: her husband. The prospect of her being made a nun, because she had married him, had suddenly moved him, taking the edge off his grievances and reviving his desire. He had started corresponding with her again, through the intermediary of a virtuous friend, Countess Langosco-Solera. In spite of his piety, he rebelled against what seemed to him a misuse of the Holy See—indeed, an attack on its honour and a piece of hypocrisy. But the virtues of Countess Langosco-Solera had little influence on him compared with the fascinating vices of Countess Sala.

At all events, the relationship between Don Vincenzo and the Little Marquis was from now on no longer the subject of gossip; on June 3 del Vasto married Princess Lavinia della Rovere, and consummated the marriage on the first night. It was really rather an unusual marriage, for the wife was the daughter of the Duchess of Urbino, Margherita Farnese's aunt, and had been betrothed to Don Giacomo Buoncompagni. The tangle of rivalries and morals occasionally permitted the mingling of fortunes, too.

Don Guglielmo paid no attention to his son's

repentance; the consummation of del Vasto's marriage gave him new energy. Even before Gregory xiii's verdict, he had begun negotiations for a new daughter-in-law—negotiations which made him pretty sure what the verdict would be. The Grand Duke of Tuscany, Francesco I de' Medici, had agreed to resume discussions about his eldest daughter, Eleonora; and this had brought over to the Gonzagas his brother, Cardinal Ferdinando de' Medici, who had the ear of the Pope.

In return, the Gonzagas had won over to the Medicis Cardinal d'Este, the Duke of Ferrara's brother. This prince of the Church had hitherto been an opponent of Cardinal de' Medici; their reconciliation had caused the defeat of Cardinal Farnese in the Consistory. It would also result in a marriage between Don Cesare d'Este and Virginia de' Medici, Cosimo i's daughter by his second wife, Camilla Martelli; this marriage would take place after that between Don Vincenzo and Donna Eleonora.

Thanks to Cavriani, his representative in Parma, the Duke of Mantua was not unaware that his daughter-in-law was being stubborn. But he was certain that she could be made to obey. The evangelistic Archbishop of Milan; the devout Duchess of Urbino; and the dauntless Duchess of Parma, a holder of the Golden Rose, who had once put down a rebellion in the Netherlands: these three would be able to persuade her—or force her—to remain a virgin.

Meanwhile her obstinacy was serving to increase her successor's dowry. Don Guglielmo stuck to a figure of 300,000 crowns, to compensate him, as he put it, for what he had repaid the Duke of Parma. He walked on air when he learned from Cardinal Gonzaga that the Grand Duke was willing to pay this amount. However, the Medicis suspended negotiations until the day Donna Margherita took her vows. To hasten that day, Don Guglielmo sent his Prime Minister, Mgr Zibramonti, Bishop of Alba, to see her.

Cardinal Borromeo had gained a victory: he had won over Mgr Ferdinando Farnese, Donna Margherita's cousin, who pleaded, not only with her, but also with her grandfather and her father. The latter's reply arrived from the Netherlands. He advised his daughter to take the veil, 'since it had pleased God to place in her such an impediment.' This advice amounted to an order. Pale as death, Donna Margherita announced to the Archbishop, the two bishops, and her aunt that, as a child, she had made a vow to be a daughter of St Benedict. They congratulated her. Duke Ottavio was less warm; Ranuccio chaffed her about the impaired virginity she was offering the Lord, and sang her the Florentine song of the 'nuns outside the convent':

> We are truly sorry
> That we are not married.
> We were really ill-advised
> To put on these habits.
> A curse be on our parents
> For sticking us inside!

Next day, Cardinal Borromeo, Mgr Farnese, and Mgr Zibramonti took her to the Benedictine nuns of St Paul, in the town of Parma. The choice of this order and this convent seemed an ironic tribute to Gregory XIII's granddaughter. The visiting room was decorated with frescoes by Correggio, almost worthy of the Palazzo del Té in Mantua, depicting Diana, Minerva, the Graces, and

Adonis. There were Cupids, too, displaying their fronts and their backs.

Donna Margherita had to be exempted from two conditions laid down by the Council of Trent for monastic vows: that the person taking them should have reached the age of sixteen and should have completed a year's novitiate. There was no need to wait for the arrival of these dispensations from Rome. The Pope had already signed them, and the Archbishop of Milan had them in his pocket.

Costly furniture and silverplate softened the vow of poverty; amiable Sisters, the vow of chastity; various privileges granted by the Abbess, the vow of obedience.

On October 28, 1583, in the chapel of St Paul, in the presence of Mgr Farnese, Mgr Zibramonti, the Duchess of Parma, and the Duchess of Urbino, Cardinal Borromeo cut off the hair of the ex-Princess of Mantua. He put on her head the black Benedictine veil and slipped on her finger the gold ring of her new, everlasting marriage. She burst into tears when the 'Te Deum' was intoned and the bells started chiming. She had taken the enigmatic name of Sister Maura Lucenia.

Part Two

1

The Duke of Mantua and the Grand Duke of Tuscany applauded from afar. Don Vincenzo resigned himself. Cardinal Gonzaga told Mgr Zibramonti, under the seal of secrecy of the Holy Office, that, at the Consistory to be held at the end of the year, he would be transferred from his bishopric of Alba to the more important one of Casale. Cardinal Cesi, being Legate at Bologna, was halfway between Florence and Mantua, so Don Francesco de' Medici appointed him to negotiate the marriage contract with Mgr Zibramonti, the Mantuan representative. The Gonzagas forgave the Legate for revealing that Don Vincenzo had given the French disease to a virgin, since this was one of the pieces of evidence that had enlightened the Consistory.

At their first meeting, Cardinal Cesi told the

Bishop of Alba that he had to transmit to him the strangest request that one ecclesiastic had ever transmitted to another. It was, however, the Medicis' prerequisite for the continuation of the negotiations. They required Don Vincenzo to prove his virility with a virgin—in front of witnesses.

This demand was not merely a pretext to guarantee Donna Eleonora's happiness. It was designed to avenge the scurrilous remarks that the Duke of Mantua had made about the Grand Duke's marriage. The widower of Joan of Austria had married his mistress, Bianca Cappello, herself the widow of a young Florentine who had abducted her to Florence when she was fifteen. This escapade, followed by her intrigue with the then Grand Prince of Tuscany, now the Grand Duke, had led to her being regarded as an adventuress. Though he had not married her until he had persuaded the Venetian Senate to style her 'true and special daughter of the Republic'—a signal honour conferred on Venetian women who married royalty—he had been severely criticized at the other Italian courts, especially that of his brother-in-law, Don Guglielmo. To be sure,

Donna Bianca's husband had been murdered in Florence, and his wife and the Grand Duke had been suspected of complicity. But this suspicion had not prevented Gregory XIII from sending the new Grand Duchess a mother-of-pearl cup, exhibited in her chamber at the Pitti palace.

The Medicis were sure that the dowry of 300,000 crowns would bring Don Guglielmo over to their way of thinking. And if he did agree to the condition they imposed, they would gratify their taste for the licentious pranks that were traditional in Florence. Tuscan poetry, notably the masterpieces of Canon Berni, was full of double meanings that amused the whole of Italy, as did the frolics of the Florentine carnival.

Mgr Zibramonti knew the Tuscan court and had a good idea what lay behind this incredible request. The Cardinal, for his part, had foreseen the Bishop's objection: dared the Grand Duke doubt a virility that the Pope himself had guaranteed? The Cardinal replied to this casuistically: first of all, the Consistory had been held in secret, and the Grand Duke was not supposed to know about it; then again, the de-

cree of April 11 referred only to the state of
affairs existing before that date; finally, it certi-
fied Don Vincenzo's virility only in his relations with Margherita Farnese. The Prince had
been vindicated before God; now he had to
vindicate himself before men.

The Bishop of Alba pointed out that the
Holy Father, in granting Don Vincenzo the
expected permission to remarry, was attesting
his virility *in virginem*. Cardinal Cesi silenced
him: Gregory XIII had spoken of remarriage,
but had not specified to whom. It was up to
Don Vincenzo to decide, in his heart of hearts,
whether he was capable of marrying a virgin,
or whether it would not be more prudent to
marry a widow. The Grand Duke, having
nothing but a virgin to offer, was simply taking
precautions.

It was all the more necessary for him to take
precautions since a second marriage would be
indissoluble. He would never let his daughter
go into a convent so that the Prince of Mantua
might take a third wife; and any proceedings
on the ground of impotence would not release
her from a husband who had the Consistory

prejudiced in his favour. The only possibility of solving the question was a public test.

Mgr Zibramonti was not yet defeated. He put forward a moral argument: was it fitting that a shameful deed should precede the sacrament of marriage? The Legate replied that he had had the same scruple and had mentioned it to his Medici colleague; but the Senior Deacon had not found this an unconscionable condition.

It would have been ungracious for Mgr Zibramonti to go on raising difficulties. He knew the virtues of Cardinal Cesi, the light of the Bolognese Church; and at Rome, during Holy Year, he had admired the virtues of Cardinal de' Medici. This noble Cardinal had washed the feet of hundreds of pilgrims, with a humility which had converted a Lutheran minister who was mingling, diabolically, with the faithful. The Bishop of Alba promised, therefore, to transmit the request to Mantua.

Don Guglielmo, who would have to make the decision, was also a model of piety. He would have been a model of humility, too, if he had not taken a fancy to being styled 'Highness,' a title he was not entitled to. Good advice was not lacking. Cardinal Gonzaga, formerly the Admiral of the Malta galleys, often spoke like a sailor instead of a priest. But Don Guglielmo's other relatives were there to give him guidance: Mgr Fedele Gonzaga, formerly Bishop of Auxerre, now Bishop of Mantua; Mgr Claudio Gonzaga, formerly majordomo to Gregory XIII; Canon Marco Antonio Gonzaga, Primicerius of the Church of St Andrew; and Fr Francesco Gonzaga, Minister General of the Minorites. Moreover, the Franciscans had provided the Duke with a scrupulous confessor, the famous Fr Panigarola.

The reply from Mantua was not long delayed. Cardinal Gonzaga was inclined to accept; but Mgr Fedele Gonzaga, Mgr Claudio Gonzaga, Canon Gonzaga, Fr Gonzaga, and Fr Panigarola protested fiercely. They demanded that the Grand Duke's demand should be submitted to the Holy Father.

2

On December 12, 1583, at a secret Consistory, Gregory XIII created nineteen new cardinals—

the longest list of promotions during his pontificate. Among them were Mgr Alessandro de' Medici,[1] Archbishop of Florence and cousin of the Senior Deacon and the Grand Duke; Mgr Castagna,[2] former Governor of Fano and Counsellor to the Holy Office; Mgr Sfondrati,[3] Bishop of Cremona; Mgr Facchinetti,[4] Patriarch of Jerusalem; and Mgr Salviati, a Florentine nobleman, the former Nuncio in France and the promoter of the St Bartholomew massacre. The nineteen also included three young men: Mgr Radziwill, Coadjutor to the Bishop of Vilna; Mgr de Joyeuse, Archbishop of Narbonne; and Captain General Sforza de Santa Fiora, the brother-in-law of the Pope's son. Once again, since it was Advent, all the cardinals were in purple.

The Pope began by silencing the newcomers. He prohibited them from uttering an opinion in the Consistory; their mouths would be opened in the following month, however.

Next, they filled the vacant bishoprics—Capri, Chioggia, Ypres, Zamora—and made various transfers. Mgr Zibramonti was translated from Alba to Casale.

[1] The future Leo XI.
[2] The future Urbanus VII.
[3] The future Gregory XIV.
[4] The future Innocent IX.

75

Then the Prince's person came up for discussion again. The cardinals returned, from a different point of view, to the question of an examination, or testimony by seven witnesses, which they had voted down at the previous Consistory. It was sought to use the Holy Office as a cloak for what was called, in civil and religious law, the test by congress. In the Hall of the Parrots, where his mouth was not shut, Cardinal de Joyeuse had cited a case that was famous in France. A few years earlier, Etienne de Bray, Treasurer of Paris, had been accused of impotence by his wife, Marie de Corbie, had been allowed to undergo this test, and had made three attempts. However, although fulfilling the canonical conditions of *erectio* and *emissio,* he could not manage the *introductio,* and his wife won her case. Cardinal d'Este, who had just been lavishly entertaining the new French Cardinal and his brother, the Duke of Joyeuse—the Duke's pearls had dazzled the Roman court—declared that the three conditions were fulfilled in the case of Don Vincenzo.

By now it was presumed that Don Vincenzo would receive the necessary authorization, since the cardinals who wanted him to were those who had proclaimed his virility. They were, however, obliged to fight the matter out. If a few of them did share the Bishop of Casale's scruples, they yielded to Cardinal de' Medici, who had now openly entered the lists. Gregory XIII would have hesitated; but he could refuse nothing to the Grand Duke at that moment. Despite the miracles of Fr Felice da Cantalice, the Papal States were suffering from a shortage of food, and Don Francesco had just relieved it by handing over half of Tuscany's grain reserves at a preferential price. The new cardinals, who could in theory have overturned the majority, but were compelled to stay silent, would in fact have brought a bare three allies to Cardinal Farnese: two in his capacity of Protector of Naples-Sicily and Poland—Cardinal Radziwill and the Sicilian Cardinal Tagliavia de Terranova—the third, a Spaniard, Cardinal de Castro, Archbishop of Seville.

Nevertheless the Dean of the Sacred College, whose gout was improving, was determined to say what was in his heart. His lengthy speech, delivered in Latin and attentively listened to, seemed worthy of Livy. He declared:

77

'This congress, most illustrious brethren,[5] this indecent congress that you are being asked to make lawful, is not an ordinary congress. It is not a question of husband and wife, of whom one complains of not being able to accomplish, through the fault of the other, the divine precept of marriage, "Increase and multiply"—a precept which is the foundation of religious and civil society, so that the theologians sometimes characterize marriage as "the womb of the Church." It is a question of prostituting an innocent virgin and permitting her to be ravished. What would St Ambrose have said of us, who, as our brother Carlo, Archbishop of Milan, has recalled, described the mere examination of a wife as "bestial"? What would St Basil have said, the immortal author of *The Integrity of Virgins?* What would St Cyprian have said, the admirable author of *The Habits of Virgins?* What would St Augustine have said, who, in *The City of God,* took care to note that "where there is no fear of punishment, these permitted pleasures still shrink from the public eye. . . . For even shameless men call this shameful; and though they love

[5] The cardinals had not yet become 'most eminent.'

78

the pleasure, dare not display it. . . . Before the bridegroom fondles his bride, does he not exclude the attendants, and even the paranymphs, and such friends as the closest ties have admitted to the bridal chamber?"

'Where are we going to find this virgin, whom it is desired to sacrifice, and sacrifice in public? From what family, however low it may have fallen, shall we have the impudence to solicit her? To what mother shall we propose this infamous transaction? If there are those, alas! who profit by and make a profession of dishonouring their daughters, at least this is done behind the back of the religious and civil authorities, who justly condemn them when such shame is brought to light. But here, it is the highest council of the religious authorities themselves, it is you, most illustrious brethren, it is the Head of our Holy Mother Church, our most Holy Father Gregory, gloriously reigning, which are asked to demand of a mother that her daughter be dishonoured. How disgusting!

'Perhaps, most illustrious brethren, we shall seek this virgin in one of those numerous places of refuge which our charity has built and for which it makes provision. Nay! among the virgins of Rome, whom our most Holy Father Gregory, gloriously reigning, annually dowers, with august generosity, for marriage or for the cloister. Thus we shall incur censure, since we shall have corrupted one of our spiritual daughters and stained with complicity a Mother Superior, a chaplain, an almoner, in short, all who will have to promote this depravity—*sollicitatio ad turpitudinem*. Do I need to recite our canons to you, most illustrious brethren? The guilty priest is deprived of his office, must do penance for fifteen years, must go on pilgrimage after pilgrimage, and end his miserable days in the deepest retreat. The guilty bishop retains his See, where he is the consecrated successor to the Apostles; but he too must do fifteen years' penance, drinking the water of anguish and eating the bread of sorrow.

'Worse still, most illustrious brethren: let us not hope to conceal this scandal from Christendom. It will feed the malice of the faithful no less than the wickedness of heretics. Let us no longer delude ourselves that we can bury this scandal in our consciences, even if our Most

Holy Father Gregory, gloriously reigning, should exempt us from censure through the power of St Peter's keys. St Paul, in his second Epistle to the Corinthians, laid it down that we must never give cause for scandal.

'And for whom should we be failing in our ministry? For a young harum-scarum who ought to have won our esteem by following his wife's example and knocking at the door of a house of God. We have spent enough time already on his person. Let him ponder the words of the psalm: "My loins are filled with illusions"—*Lumbi mei impleti sunt illusionibus!*'

It seemed at first as if Cardinal Farnese's eloquence had convinced all his colleagues, especially since, in contrast with the preceding Consistory, there was no discussion. The *Quid vobis videtur?* fell into the silence. When the supporters of the test by congress stood up, their hats in their hands, the Dean and Vice Chancellor thought for a moment that he had triumphed. The number of cardinals remaining seated and covered seemed higher—but he was including those whose mouths were shut. Once again, Cardinal Farnese was defeated.

Once again, Gregory XIII, wearing the gold-embroidered mitre, intoned the words that the Holy Ghost had inspired. The Prince of Mantua was authorized to prove before witnesses his virility *in virginem;* and those who would have to participate were exempted from censure.

Part Three

1

Don Vincenzo, who was surprised at the Church taking such a close interest in his affairs, thought no more of Sister Maura Lucenia. At Colorno he and the del Vastos toasted the Holy Father in the course of their Tiberian amusements. The wife of the Little Marquis had been taught a thing or two by the Countess Sala, and her husband had the habit of not refusing the Prince anything. All three could have confirmed that the Prince could fulfil the three canonical conditions for virility; but none of them had proof of his virility *in virginem*. Setting up a new establishment was a matter of some importance to the young Prince; his father, having granted him an apanage while he was a husband, had cut him down to the monthly allowance of 500 crowns.

Meanwhile, at Pisa, the Grand Duke welcomed Cardinal Cesi on his return from the Consistory and, as a token of his gratitude, made him Protector of the Knights of St Stephen, whose headquarters was in that town. This order, founded by Cosimo I and dedicated to one of the patron saints of Florence, was designed to combat the Berber pirates after the fashion of the old Order of Rhodes and Malta and the Order of St George of Ravenna, founded by Paul III. Its members had had the glory of relieving the Knights of St John when they were besieged at Valette, and they had distinguished themselves in the battle of Lepanto. In the Grand Duke's estimation, a prince of the Church who had helped to win a tough battle was not unworthy to be their Protector. As Grand Master, he put the golden collar round Cardinal Cesi's neck, and Tomasso de' Medici, the Admiral of St Stephen, put the white cloak round his shoulders.

Into the bargain, the Grand Duke gave him 3,000 crowns for his good works. This was exactly the sum for which the Legate had been praying to the Lord, so that he could round off and embellish the possessions of the Oratorian fathers, for whom he had a soft spot. The

Prince's person had produced manna from heaven for their Church of St Mary in Vallicella.

Don Francesco and the Cardinal discussed where the test by congress could be held. The Grand Duke, who wanted to rule out any deception, would willingly have proposed Florence, and would have volunteered to be a witness. The Cardinal would likewise have proposed Bologna—without going so far as to volunteer as a witness, but guaranteeing complete security. So secret must the spectacle be, that it could not take place on the territories of the Grand Duke or of the Pope. At Mantua, they would have been in the Gonzaga country; at Urbino, in the home town of Margherita Farnese's cousin, the Marchioness del Vasto's brother. Venice was the city of a thousand ruses. The Cardinal suggested Ferrara, although this was one of Don Vincenzo's places of amusement and the Duchess was his sister. Don Francesco approved of this suggestion: Don Alphonso, twice a widower, had twice been his brother-in-law and had remained on the best of terms with him. The ancient Valois family, and Lucrezia Borgia's grandson, would be bound to enjoy such a story. Besides, Cardinal d'Este would be a natural ally. Finally, the Bishop of Modena, Cardinal Canano, a Ferrarese nobleman, owed it to Cardinals d'Este and Cesi that he had been made a cardinal on December 12. Cardinal Cesi would ask him to keep a discreet eye on the propriety of the proceedings. After all, must not every father in the purple defend the honour of the entire Consistory? 'Since it will be in Ferrara,' said the Grand Duke, 'let us hope for a Ferrarese fig for this Mantuan bean.' The Cardinal pretended not to know the saying about figs and beans.

Don Francesco handed him, to be passed on to Mgr Zibramonti, the clauses that had been agreed on the subject of the dowry. The figure had been approved, but the attention to tiny details in these clauses recalled that the Medicis had been bankers and merchants before becoming Grand Dukes.

The 300,000 gold crowns would be paid at Mantua, a third on the celebration of the marriage, a third after one year, and the remainder after three years. The dowry would be secured in the State of Mantua upon landed property worth at least 450,000 crowns. If the Princess died before her husband and childless—'which God forbid!' said the text—half of the amount would go back to the Medicis, notwithstanding any statute of the State of Mantua, and the rest would go to the Prince, provided he had consummated the marriage.

If the Duke objected to the return of half the dowry, the Grand Duke would pay only 250,-000 crowns, and, in that case, if the Princess died childless before her husband—'which God forbid!'—the Duke would not have to pay back anything. But if the Prince died before his wife, with children or childless—'which God forbid!'—the Princess would retain the dowry, notwithstanding any statute of the State of Mantua. As to her clothes, ornaments, and jewels, they would not be included in the dowry and she could dispose of them as she wished.

It was for Don Guglielmo to fix the amount of the counterdowry. If the Prince should die, with children or childless—'which God forbid!'—the Princess would have the life interest, unless she remarried without having had a child.

The Duke would also determine what provision was necessary for his daughter-in-law's petty expenses. Nevertheless, he was invited to state a figure, since it was best that there should be 'nothing undecided between friends and beloved kinsfolk.'

The cost of transporting the Princess and her attendants to the State of Mantua would devolve upon the Grand Duke. The cost of the marriage—Don Vincenzo and Donna Eleonora were cousins—would be borne jointly. Letters in identical terms would announce the union to the Emperor and to the King of Spain.

In cauda venenum. It was laid down, in conclusion, that 'the noble Prince's virility and fitness for marriage will have to be made clear beforehand, according to the terms agreed in a separate clause.'

Cardinal Cesi, the new Knight of St Stephen, went on his way to Bologna, where the new Bishop of Casale was waiting for him. The Grand Duke accompanied him as far as the St Gal gate, then returned to the Pitti palace to read to the Grand Duchess one of their favourite poems, the *Capitolo About Spindles*. This work of Ruscelli had been published in Venice three years before. Some lines seemed to comment on the reasons for the test to which the Medicis, with the help of Gregory XIII, were submitting the Prince of Mantua:

> The spindle is honoured
> More than the lance or the sword. . . .
> But some kinds are disappointing.
> Gentle ladies, good spinners,
> Push these away quickly,
> Do not waste time handling them.

2

Though it would be exempt from censure, Don Guglielmo still hesitated about accepting the test by congress. His oracle, Fr Panigarola, was less complacent than the Pope and the College of Cardinals, and told him that a tormenting attack of gout was a sign from heaven.

Mgr Zibramonti had been supporting the Franciscan's efforts. He had deferred to Cardinal Cesi, but had maintained his own opinion. While sacrificing himself for his master, he felt embarrassed by a rôle which he called 'alien to his character.' Writing from Bologna, he had not hidden from him his reluctance to 'deal with such an odious subject.' In the hope of rendering the congress superfluous, he had secured from Don Cesare a certificate of the Prince's virility *in virginem*. When he received it, after the Legate's departure for the Consistory of December 12, he forwarded it to him at full speed. But this document, sent from Ferrara on the 11th, had not reached Rome until the 15th.

'I hereby declare,' wrote Don Cesare, 'that the person of H.H. the Prince of Mantua can be excited like that of any other man, and that H.H. can make carnal use of a woman, virgin or otherwise, as readily as anybody else. . . .'

These words had come too late to enlighten the Fathers in the purple; would they have any effect on the Grand Duke? Cardinal Cesi disillusioned Mgr Zibramonti. He had sent a Latin translation of the document to the Cardinal Camerlengo of the Sacred College and to the Pope's house steward. He, like them, had been glad to see that it confirmed what Cardinal d'Este and he had reported to the first

Consistory; but all of them had been of the opinion that it would not have altered the voting at the second one.

To comfort himself, the Bishop asked the Legate whether, in the translation, he had styled Don Vincenzo *Sua Celsitudo,* i.e., his Highness. Such flattery, so agreeable to Don Guglielmo, was current among the Italian princes, but was recognized neither in Rome, nor in Madrid, nor in Vienna. It was the result of the title of Grand Duke having been granted, first by Pius v, of blessed memory, to Don Francesco's father, then by the Emperor Maximilian to Don Francesco himself. The other dukes, for want of being grand dukes, claimed 'Highness,' the corollary of that title; but Don Francesco and his wife exercised much ingenuity in thwarting their efforts. The 'daughter of the Republic' had prevented the Venetian Senate from granting the designation to the Duke of Ferrara; Don Francesco himself had prevented his nephew, the new Emperor Rudolf, from granting it to the Duke of Mantua. They rather suspected that Don Guglielmo would try to snatch this honour from them on the occasion of the marriage, but they meant to make him pay through the nose for it. Cardinal Cesi replied to the Bishop of Casale that he had taken care not to lend Don Vincenzo a debatable title; not once, throughout the two Consistories, had the Prince of Mantua been styled *Celsitudo*—not even by Cardinal Gonzaga.

Cardinal Cesi made it clear that the Grand Duke, while considering the certificate of December 11 to be a dead letter, was not challenging Don Cesare, but recognized him in advance as an important witness. The Cardinal asked the Bishop to urge the Gonzagas not to evade the issue any longer. Don Vincenzo would have to comply with the Pope's wishes, as humbly as Donna Margherita had done.

3

And the Gonzagas gave way. The Bologna negotiations were concluded, and Don Guglielmo recalled Mgr Zibramonti, who took his leave of Cardinal Cesi. The two ecclesiastics did not part company without exchanging compliments. Since the disappearance of the Eagle of Italy, founded in the tenth century by the first Gonzaga, there had been no Mantuan order; but in Bologna there still existed the Order of St Mary of the Tower, otherwise known as the Brethren of the Jubilation. Created for the defence of widows and orphans, it seemed made for the occasion. The Legate, protector of the law, invested Mgr Zibramonti in the grey mantle of St Mary of the Tower; and Mgr Zibramonti, on behalf of his master, presented the Legate with a cask of Lambrusco, the red sparkling wine of Modena. Meanwhile, Don Guglielmo had sent his cousin, Carlo Gonzaga, to Florence to reach final agreement on the clauses relating to the dowry. He had initialled them on January 10, 1584.

The Grand Duke was left free, whether to pay 300,000 crowns, with the option of recovering half that amount if the Princess died without issue, or to pay only 200,000 crowns. The counterdowry would come to 15,000 crowns, the same as it had been 'for the noble Duchess, the daughter of the Emperor Ferdinand.' But, whereas the Grand Duke would have liked to make preparations for the wedding at his leisure, and to celebrate it after Easter, the Duke, always anxious about his health, wanted it to take place before Lent began on February 22. Moreover, he wanted the ceremony to take place in Mantua, so as to wipe out the memory of the previous one. 'As to the noble Prince's competence with virgins, he was prepared to rely on him.' Don Carlo, to whom Don Vincenzo had given every piece of information that seemed useful, knew what he was undertaking when he signed the 'separate clause' left in the Grand Duke's hands: 'The noble Don Alfonso d'Este, or his son Don Cesare, in whom we have complete confidence, must testify to the virility and aptitude of the noble Prince of Mantua with a virgin, in a test that is witnessed personally. Failing which, the marriage will not take place.'

Cardinal Cesi and Mgr Zibramonti were falling out of the picture, but two other cardinals, and Mgr Leoni, Bishop of Ferrara, were becoming more prominent. From Rome, Cardinal d'Este was encouraging Don Alfonso not to refuse his services to the Medicis and the Gonzagas. He was also lecturing Mgr Leoni, in order to anticipate difficulties of the kind raised by Mgr Fedele Gonzaga in Mantua not long before. And how could he fail to have influence over the prelate who had succeeded him? The Cardinal had been Bishop of Ferrara at the age of fifteen.

Cardinal Canano, his colleague in Modena, had not waited for the Holy Father to open his mouth for him on January 9 before starting to spread the good news. Mgr Leoni, too, was imbued with his own importance: beneath his crosier were Ariosto's birthplace, Tasso's prison, the meetingplace of a famous Council; to these would now be added a no less historic congress. He might even gain a cardinal's hat out of it! The Pope had lit the candles; the College of Cardinals had made the bed; a Prince was to lie in it; a reigning duke or his heir would keep the garments, like Saul at the stoning of St Stephen. And, as if that were not enough, the Grand Duke had just decided that his ambassador at Ferrara, the knight Urbani, should be one of the party.

4

The ambassador's instructions reached him on the evening of January 11. They concerned, above all, the choice of the young woman, who had to be 'a virgin, healthy and not suspect.' Don Francesco added: 'We shall reward her in whatever way you decide with the noble Duke. Do not trouble yourself about the amount, but about her virginity.'

The ambassador smiled when he read the concluding words: 'We venture to hope that everything will be done with as little publicity as possible.' That was going to be a difficult task, in a town where everything the Church did echoed sixteen times. The Prince had scarcely arrived, and already there was no one who did not know why he was there. The Governor of Mantua, Don Luigi Olivo, acted as his guide—to prevent him from wasting his ammunition on the sparrows.

Don Alfonso had also received a letter from Florence. On the morning of January 12, he summoned the ambassador. The Duke was very conscious of his responsibilities towards the Gonzagas, and was no less concerned about the Medicis: Don Cesare's marriage to Donna Virginia was bound up with the success of the test. As far as keeping the secret was concerned, he was no longer in a position to guarantee it.

When he compared his letter with Urbani's, he noticed some slight differences, and he asked the knight to draw up a memorandum to reconcile them. Urbani set out the following five points:

First, the girl would be 'seen and examined by two physicians, two nurses, and two matrons, in the presence of Don Alfonso, Don Cesare, and the knight Urbani.'

Secondly, Don Alfonso would guard her strictly 'until she was approached by the noble Prince.' She would be locked in a room with barred windows and only one door. The Belfiore castle, quite near Ferrara, had been put at the disposal of the two jousters.

Thirdly, the jousts would take place in a single night.

Fourthly, the Prince, in deflowering the girl, would use 'neither his fingers, nor any instru-

99

ment or contrivance, nor anything that is not solely of his virtue.'

Fifthly, those who had testified to the virginity would verify the defloration.

Don Alfonso dictated an addendum. He reserved for his son the right which the special clause shared between them: Don Cesare would 'see with his eyes and touch with his hands, as much as he wished, the noble Prince's person.'

Such was the diplomatic document signed at Ferrara on Thursday, January 12. The Bishop had not co-operated in drawing up the text, but he put his *nihil obstat* on it. Unable to be one of the witnesses, since Cardinal Cesi would have heard about it in Bologna, he felt sure, at any rate, that his own physician would accept.

Now they had to find the girl. Don Alfonso had had a word with the Marchioness of Carrara, who was visiting the court and had put some orphans in a Farrarese foundling hospital. But the ambassador, filled with enthusiasm, jumped the gun.

That very afternoon he disguised himself and went to the house of a Roman lady whose name he had been given. She was the widow of the architect Ligorio, who designed St Peter's and the new wing of the Vatican. He had died, the previous year, in Ferrara, where he had been in charge of some building work for Don Alfonso. His widow, who was without means, had several daughters as modest as they were pretty. According to what the ambassador wrote to the Grand Duke, this deserving family was dependent on the brother of the Bishop of Carpentras, Count Scipione del Sacrato, 'an elderly nobleman who delighted in charitable deeds.'

The widow Ligorio lived near the Hospital of St Anne, where Tasso was locked up. The knight had recently visited the poet with a present from the Grand Duchess—twenty-five ducats and a silver cup—to thank him for some sonnets.

The ambassador knocked on the widow's door, told her who he was, put a well-lined purse on the table, and spoke rather cryptically about an affair of State which concerned two crowns and which had the blessing of the Holy See. This affair, he went on, required the self-sacrifice of a decent virgin, who would be rewarded with a good dowry and a good marriage. When the widow asked if he were referring to Don Vincenzo, he thought it pointless to deny it; but, for form's sake, he swore her to secrecy. Nothing short of a prince and a pope, she declared, would induce her to act against her principles. Her daughters were 'accustomed to saying their prayers on their knees, their rosaries in their hands.' Then, uttering a sigh, she brought them in. The eldest seemed the most attractive. The ambassador asked the mother to give her a bath, tidy her up, and await his instructions. He was overjoyed at having done a good job for his master—and, no doubt, for himself as well.

He wanted to surprise Don Alfonso and Don Cesare with the speed of his transaction. But he could not find them; they had taken the Prince out hunting. That evening, a servant of Count Scipione del Sacrato brought him back his purse and told him that the widow Ligorio's eldest daughter had set out with that pious nobleman for an unknown destination.

5

On the morning of Friday, January 13, the ambassador, still in disguise for the sake of discretion, returned to the ducal palace. The Duke, also disguised, was just leaving to go shopping at the fish market. This was his custom on Fridays; he was fond of fish, and he trusted no one else to choose it. His disguise, like those of his attendants, seemed as open as the Grand Duke's secret—but it did allow the fishwives, of whom he was no less fond, to make bawdy jokes in front of him. And they had plenty of material, with ribald references to the Prince of Mantua's 'fish.'

The ambassador, falling into step with the Duke's party, recalled the Florentine carnival songs about anglers, crabbers, and frog catchers, in which Neptune and the naiads competed with Pomona and Priapus at the game of innuendo. The fishwives, too, sang a smutty song:

Fishing is the sovereign art—
Netting fish or tickling them—
But it's no good casting your net
If the fish does not go in.

The net that the ambassador had cast had
slipped out of his fingers, and he was anxious
to know whether the Duke or the Marchioness
had been any luckier.

After the menservants had put the Duke's
fish in their baskets, he bowed to Don Alfonso,
who told him why, the previous evening, he
had offered Don Vincenzo only the pleasures
of hunting. Governor Olivo had persuaded the
Prince that he should not agree to the test in a
single night, and Don Alfonso had sent to Florence for the Grand Duke's opinion on this
point. His son's right to see and touch had not
been disputed. On the other hand, the Governor had suggested that they make do with
one physician, one matron, and one nurse, so as
not to have too many witnesses.

Besides, said the Duke, the Carrara virgins
were either too cold or not attractive enough,
and they would have to look elsewhere. The
knight preferred not to mention his failure

with the widow Ligorio, but he soon found that nothing could be kept dark in Ferrara. With a laugh, Don Alfonso cursed that old rascal del Sacrato, who had cut the ground from under their feet. The ambassador gave a sickly smile.

During the day, there was a new stir. A message came from the palace, warning him that Don Vincenzo had just announced the marriage. Although this was not so secret as the rest of the negotiations, it did depend on a condition that had not yet been fulfilled. Was the Prince shouting victory before the battle to show that he was sure of winning?—or to quell the rumours, as if the test had already taken place? Urbani did not hide the truth from the Grand Duke; he admitted that 'the very stones know the story.' Don Vincenzo's indiscretion and rashness prompted him to add this remark: 'If the test does not succeed, which God forbid, the foresight of your Most Serene Highness will be the more praised, and these Mantuan lords will be the more blamed.'

The Grand Duke's reply to Don Alfonso arrived two days later. He thanked 'his Most Illustrious Lordship for his very amiable diligence,' apologized for causing him so much trouble, and insisted that the test should be carried out in a single night. And he 'prayed to the Lord God to have the Prince in His holy care' on that night.

6

On January 19, Don Vincenzo took his leave of his brother-in-law and his sister. He agreed with the Governor of Mantua in rejecting a condition that he found unacceptable. Don Alfonso told him that a very charming girl had been found for him—a Ferrarese fig. He would not even condescend to see her. Urbani, dismayed, reported to the Grand Duke that, according to rumour, the Prince was thinking of withdrawing into a monastery, like his ex-wife. Was Cardinal Farnese's wish about to come true?

The facts were quite otherwise. After sending his mentor to inform his father, Don Vincenzo had left for Mirandola, where the Marquis del Vasto, without the Marchioness, was waiting for him. The two cousins wanted to persuade the noble lady in those parts not to hand over to Henri III of France one of her sons, whose good looks were famous and who, as Cardinal Cesi had told the Consistory, had been cured of the French disease by Master Beato of Bologna. The name of this disease should have been enough to make the French court suspicious, but Mgr de Foix, Archbishop of Toulouse and French ambassador at Rome, was pestering the Countess to give this treasure of hers to the Most Christian King. Thanks to del Vasto and Don Vincenzo, Henri III was no more successful than with the special jubilee designed to obtain 'a handsome Dauphin.'

On January 21 the Duke of Mantua, grief-stricken, wrote to Don Carlo, his representative with the Grand Duke. He told him that his son had left Ferrara without attempting the test, and that the Governor, Don Luigi, was galloping towards the Arno to propose a compromise. His intentions had not changed, but he wanted to dodge the risks that lay in too strict a test. He did not fail to emphasize his magnanimity over 'something that has never been demanded for any marriage, especially between princes.'

At Ferrara, Don Alfonso was just as upset as Don Guglielmo. When Don Vincenzo left he was seized by a fever—no doubt because he saw Don Cesare's marriage in jeopardy. He received the Grand Duke's ambassador in his bedroom. They lamented about the Prince's escapade, but did not conclude that there was nothing further they could do. If the third article in the agreement were amended, the Prince was prepared to come to heel. So Don Alfonso kept the Ferrarese virgin at Belfiore, with the nurse and the matron, under the supervision of the Bishop's doctor. Yet, in spite of the glory of verifying a defloration by his master's future son-in-law, the ambassador advised the Grand Duke to choose another town for the test if it did in fact take place. He no longer thought it possible in Ferrara; the widow Ligorio had rather put him off the place.

The Grand Duke replied to his ambassador and to Don Alfonso in roughly the same terms. The Prince's departure had made him 'very suspicious.' He was disturbed by all this panic about a single night. 'If a young man of twenty-one feels himself incapable of proving his virility in a single night, what guarantee is there that he will prove it in several?' Don Francesco demanded. As Urbani had suggested, he was glad he had been so exacting. But he did not feel that the scheme had fallen through, any more than Don Guglielmo did. He asked, however, that, if the Prince returned, nothing should be done without his instructions.

The ambassador told the Grand Duke two significant anecdotes. Don Cesare and his friends were eating truffles—which ladies never ate in public, out of modesty—when one of them observed that he really had no need of this aphrodisiac. Then he turned to Urbani and quipped: 'But there is somebody who might have great need of them.' The knight was astonished that Don Cesare, after giving the Prince a certificate of virility, now seemed to be contradicting it.

A little later, in the same place, they were teasing a young Ferrarese woman who had married a Mantuan, and the ambassador defended her by saying that 'everything from Mantua is beautiful and good.' At which a gentleman in waiting exclaimed: 'Everything is beautiful, certainly, but not quite everything is good.' 'And they all burst out laughing'—which was scarcely a compliment to Don Vincenzo.

The Bishop, for his part, was no longer so happy about giving his support to an act decided on by a secret Consistory. Count Scipione del Sacrato, in an indignant letter, had denounced the attempt to seduce an innocent virgin and begged him to remove from Ferrara a test which disturbed the peace of the soul. Fearfully, Mgr Leoni calculated the difficulties of the affair he had to supervise. Far from winning him a cardinal's hat, it looked like it was costing him one. Cardinal d'Este and Cardinal Canano had pushed him forward, but were by no means anxious to take his place. Each of them had postponed a journey to Ferrara—yet the Bishop knew how eager Cardinal Canano was to celebrate mass in the cathedral of his native town.

7

All these rumours came to Don Guglielmo's ears and stirred him to hasten his son's vindication, which to him signified, not a humiliating test, but the glorious marriage that would crown it. The idea that the Grand Duke might renounce the marriage gave him more pain than the gout.

Fearing that the Governor of Mantua was not a skilful enough diplomatist, he sent him, as an assistant, his most trusted confidant, Mgr Camillo Capilupi, the Pope's Referendary. This prelate, the brother of the Prince's steward, had been Mantuan ambassador in France at the time of the St Bartholomew massacre. He had published a famous account of the massacre, which he described as a 'stratagem' of Charles ix and 'the most beautiful enterprise in Christendom.' He would feel proud to be associated with his colleagues in Casale and Ferrara, and with Cardinals Canano, d'Este, Gonzaga, de' Medici, Borromeo, and Cesi, in a 'stratagem' of a different kind. 'It will be as if I myself were speaking to the Grand Duke,' wrote Don Guglielmo to Don Carlo.

Chided by Fr Panigarola, he made a desperate effort to prevent the test taking place. Since the Grand Duke wanted to save his daughter from 'the risk of having to return to her parents' or taking the veil, Don Guglielmo swore, through Mgr Capilupi, never to have the marriage dissolved. Moreover, said the Referendary, he was sure that 'her Most Serene Highness did not suffer from any impediment.' To coax the Grand Duke, the prelate paid a special visit to the Grand Duchess; he presented to her, to make amends for ancient wrongs, a relic that had touched the Most Precious Blood.

But the Medicis would not budge an inch. They even confided to Mgr Capilupi that 'if the noble Prince had not made up his mind within ten or twelve days' they would consider another match. The excuse they gave for this ultimatum was that they had been patient for a very long time. The Mantuans soon learned the real reason—Carlo Emanuele of Savoy had come forward as a suitor. This duke had sought

Donna Eleonora's hand three years before; but he had also asked for a million crowns. Not having found such a sum anywhere, he was beginning his rounds again.

Mgr Capilupi knew, of course, that the Mantuan match was still the more advantageous for the Grand Duke; the ambition of the young Duke of Savoy was known and dreaded. He was already quarrelling with France over the marquisate of Saluces. He was the only Italian prince who did not view marriage as a means of preserving the status quo.

Another thing reassured the prelate. On February 1, the date of the courteous ultimatum, Don Francesco had given proof of his 'loyalty': he had written to his brothers-in-law, the archdukes, to tell them about the marriage planned between his eldest daughter and the Prince of Mantua. Moreover, he instructed his ambassador in Vienna, the knight Alberti, to make the same communication to the Emperor. These three letters, to be sure, each contained a discreet reference to 'certain difficulties which have still to be overcome.'

In vain did Mgr Capilupi, having failed to have the test abandoned, visit the Pitti Palace and the Old Palace, where Donna Bianca stayed from time to time, and argue that it should not be restricted to a single night. It was clear that the Grand Duchess derived a mischievous pleasure from arguing with a prelate like a Boccaccio heroine. But such were Florentine manners, and this affair did nothing to alter them.

Donna Bianca had been given an indult by Gregory XIII authorizing her to visit convents, in spite of the Bull banning them 'even to countesses, marchionesses, and duchesses,' on pain of excommunication. She had been able to find out, therefore, that Donna Eleonora's earthly happiness had aroused the enthusiasm of the Tuscan abbesses.

The most thrilled of all was Mother Brigida degli Albizzi, who governed the Benedictine nuns of St Paul the Greater. With her ended the tradition by which the Mother Superior of this convent was the mystical bride of the Archbishop of Florence. She had celebrated this marriage, the memory of which still disturbed her, with Mgr Altoviti, the predecessor of Cardinal Alessandro de' Medici. Each time the Grand Duchess visited her, avid for shameful secrets, she would give more details. The Archbishop had dismounted from his horse at the threshold of the church, had been censed and sprinkled with holy water, had stepped on a dais in the chancel, had sat on a throne draped with red velvet, had set Mother Brigida on his right hand, on a throne draped with green velvet, and had slipped on her finger a gold ring, the symbol of her marriage to the Florentine Church. After mass, he had gone with her to her rooms, where a banquet had been served. The canons of the cathedral, the prior, and the chaplains had fêted the couple, wished them children as numerous as those of Abraham, and left them alone together till the next day. Their wedding night, said the Abbess, had been a night of prayer; their children were not of the flesh, but of the Lord.

Mother Brigida was less seared by her memories of Mgr Altoviti than was a certain Benedictine nun by hers of the Prince of Mantua. Nevertheless she advised the Grand Duchess not to marry her stepdaughter to an impotent prince, even if the cancellation of the marriage deprived the Benedictine nuns of the hope of recruiting another princess.

8

At the same time as he dispatched Mgr Capilupi to the Grand Duke, Don Guglielmo sent Mgr Zibramonti and another of his secretaries, the Knight Gabbioneta, to Rome. His spiritual director had convinced him that the Pope and the Curia would have a change of heart. The holder of the keys had unlocked, as it were, the door to the congress chamber; was he not free to lock it again? The Consistory had not been held in public. Neither the decree about the test by congress nor the preceding one had gone through the papal datary, and it might be that no one would ever find any trace of them. Mgr Zibramonti was well aware that pontifical decisions were taken and implemented in this manner. Nevertheless, his mission seemed to him more delicate than Mgr Capilupi's: he would have to obtain a *mea culpa* from the Holy Father himself.

He had been given a means of making himself welcome: he would ask for a Bull for the erection of a Jesuits' college in Mantua, to fulfil the vow taken by the Duchess at the birth of Don Vincenzo and forgotten ever since. Gregory XIII had granted such an honour to the Society's novitiates in Poland and Japan, so this request was calculated to flatter his fondness for the Jesuits and to flatter him, too. With this ally, nothing was impossible.

The first person the Bishop of Casale saw when he reached Rome was Cardinal Gonzaga, who was resolutely hostile to the Mantuan aims, and in whose presence he would not have dared to make the slightest allusion to the test by congress. The former commander of the Malta galleys struck an unexpected note. Paraphrasing the saying he had quoted in the first Consistory, 'Unto the pure, all things are pure,' he said the Church's greatness lay in descending to the level of weak mankind in order to transform the worst miseries into instruments of sanctification. The test by congress should be judged by the light of heaven rather than by any worldly light. It would permit the Prince to marry a princess, and also to mortify his pride and atone for his sins. Like the Borromeos, Cardinal Gonzaga inscribed the word *Humilitas* under his golden crown.

Mgr Zibramonti replied that the stir this adventure had caused was mortification and atonement enough already. He read a letter from a Palermo canon to Canon Gonzaga, saying that the chapter of the cathedral and the Archbishop, Mgr Marulli, who had been at loggerheads for years, had settled their differences so as to be in a better position to comment on this astonishing news. The Cardinal begged Mgr Zibramonti to let Palermo concern itself as it pleased about the Prince's person, but to speak to the Pope only about the Bull for a new erection.

Nor did Secretary Gabbioneta hear words that were any more comforting. The Florentine merchant Antonio Bandini, trustee and accountant to the College of Cardinals, who enjoyed the right to be present at certain papal chapels, told him what he had heard as he was coming out of the one held on February 7, Gregory XIII's birthday. Like the Grand Duke, several cardinals had been expressing their amazement that a young man of Don Vincenzo's age was scared by only one night being allowed. And Cardinal Galli had declared, on the word of a secretary of state, that 'he would have persuaded the noble Prince to clear this obstacle briskly enough.'

9

The Grand Duke, too, was taking steps to prevent any sudden change in the situation. The two Medici cardinals were in Rome, the Archbishop of Florence having stayed there after the Consistory. Nevertheless, Don Francisco had instructed Cardinal Cesi to dog Mgr Zibramonti's footsteps. He relied on the zeal of his principal spokesman more than on that of his brother and his cousin.

The Legate at Bologna, like the Bishop of Casale, had an excuse for visiting the Pope. While travelling through Tuscany, he had visited Arezzo, the birthplace of Aretino. His purpose had not been to honour the memory of that licentious author, who had been made a Knight of Rhodes by Clement VII and a Knight of St Peter by Julius III. He wanted to ordain a young Bolognese who had been dear to him, and who was a novice at the Camaldolites' hermitage. Yet, under the rules of the establishment, he had been denied access to him. And even if he had been allowed in, he could not have ordained him, for, under the rules of the order, this privilege was reserved to the Prior General. With the Grand Duke's permission, the Cardinal intended to ask for a Bull granting to cardinals the privilege of entering the Camaldolites' houses offhand and ordaining them at pleasure, whatever the rules might say.

The two negotiators, who had been ordained in the same year, met face to face. Since Mgr Zibramonti had not yet been received by the Pope, Cardinal Cesi was as forthright as Cardinal Gonzaga on the question of the Prince's person.

The Bishop of Casale lacked support in another quarter. The Jesuits were well aware that they were the ostensible reason for his journey, and they were not accustomed to pulling other people's chestnuts out of the fire. Without ill feeling towards them, but not without a pang of remorse, he decided to limit his canvassing to the Bull for a new erection.

Just as he was setting out for the Quirinal, a letter came from Mantua with the news that the Medicis had made a concession to Mgr Capilupi and that the Duke had accepted it. The test would take place 'in a single night, but in three attempts,' i.e., with the possibility of two intermissions. The Bishop rejoiced at seeing the chances of his master's son increased. But his modesty was still offended, in spite of all the dukes, grand dukes, and cardinals. He prayed for a miracle that would put an end to this obscene conspiracy.

When the Pope suddenly asked him how matters stood with the test by congress, he considered himself absolved from his promise to Cardinals Gonzaga and Cesi. He said, in a rather low voice, out of respect, 'In a single night, but in three attempts,' fell on his knees, kissed the holy slippers, and implored St Longinus and St Barbara to enlighten the Vicar of Christ. He did not have to repeat the shameful words, for Gregory XIII had sharp ears. 'Be of good heart, Our son!' said the Pope, misunderstanding the Bishop's emotion. 'The time allowed seems reasonable to Us.' *Roma locuta est.*

10

If the Duke of Savoy's representations had made some impression on the Grand Duke, there were others who wanted to render the same kind of service to Don Guglielmo. The knight Calzoni, his ambassador in Venice, sent him a detailed despatch reporting the remarks and proposals of the French ambassador, Hurault de Maisse.

The envoy of the Most Christian King had not been dazzled by the test being exempted from censure, and he characterized as 'diabolical' a marriage that required a mortal sin of the bridegroom. Adding irony to a remark worthy of Mgr Zibramonti and Cardinal Farnese, he professed to be anxious to know what fiefs the Grand Duke was giving in return for such an enormity. He thought the Grand Duke had made it clear that he wanted to ridicule Don Vincenzo, who was by no means sure of getting the reward even if he passed the test. The ambassador had an alternative bride to propose: Christine of Lorraine, the Queen of France's cousin. She was, he said, the most virtuous, gracious, and beautiful princess in Christendom. Her modest dowry would be compensated for by a French alliance, which would be worth 'perhaps whole States' to Don Vincenzo. Finally, 'the great King of France' would not oblige him to prove his virility. The ambassador 'was only waiting for his Highness's commands'—he employed the flattering title—'to bring this affair, with God's help, to a successful issue.'

Although he had tricked Henri III, Don Vincenzo was attracted by France and had no objection to 'the Lorraine match.' But Don Guglielmo turned down the offer, however honourable it might be for the Gonzagas. To enhance French influence in Mantua would revive the hopes of his brother, the Duke of Nevers. This alliance, which Hurault de Maisse depicted as a 'shield,' was in fact a danger, just as a Savoyard alliance was a danger to the Grand Duke. Faithful to 'the Tuscan match,' Don Guglielmo was not afraid of treachery; the Grand Duke could hardly renounce a decision that had the backing of two Consistories.

'A single night, but in three attempts' having been accepted by everyone up to and including the Pope, Don Guglielmo urged Mgr Capilupi to fix a venue for the test. Urbani had no need to advise against Ferrara. Don Vincenzo owed Don Alfonso a grudge for not having made things easier for him, just as he owed Don Cesare a grudge for his nasty jokes. Don Guglielmo did not scruple to say that his son-in-law had the evil eye. He had been at the tournament where Henri II was mortally wounded; his first two wives had died without having children; his third wife would not have any more.

Relations between the two courts suddenly deteriorated. The Duke of Mantua withdrew from Mantuan law courts the right to judge cases in which his subjects were involved. He dismissed the Belfiore virgin, the matron, and the nurse. It was understood that the test would take place elsewhere. It soon became known that it would take place in Venice, with a whole array of precautions.

Tasso breathed poetical laments at not seeing his young patron again. Count Scipione del Sacrato returned the widow Ligorio's eldest daughter to the fold. And Mgr Leoni proclaimed that Cardinal Canano would shortly be coming from Modena to celebrate mass in full dress.

11

Donna Eleonora, the principal lady concerned, could not be unaware of a story that was known to 'the very stones' in Ferrara, and the very abbesses in Florence. Her father and stepmother had forbidden anyone to speak to her of it; but since everyone was speaking of it, it would have been hard for her not to hear about it. Fascinating, well read, already a patron of the arts, and 'sweetly tormented by her seventeen years,' she had learned these open secrets in spite of the strictness of her principal maid of honour, the Countess of Carpegna.

Her youthful attendants were on the lookout for information to impart to her. Maria,[1] her youngest sister, was a child; but Anna, the second daughter, who was fifteen and whom she

---

[1] The future wife of Henri IV of France.

loved dearly, sneaked the cardinals' and ambassadors' despatches from their father. Anna had been promised to a son of the Archduke Ferdinand, and, in the laborious negotiations over 'the Mantuan match,' she could see her own nuptials foreshadowed. Sixteen-year-old Donna Virginia, the aunt of the two girls, displayed still more curiosity, so impatient was she to be married to Don Cesare. The Grand Duke's daughters had had only one brother, Filippo, who had died a few months previously. This Grand Prince of Florence had been buried in his red velvet court dress, a little gilded rapier at his side. His death made Cardinal de' Medici the heir to the Tuscan throne, if, like the late Cardinal de Braganza, King of Portugal, he could obtain the Pope's dispensation to renounce the purple. The Grand Duchess, who had a daughter and a son by her first husband, seemed condemned to barrenness with her second. Her countless novenas in the convents, the scapulars she wore, the gypsies she consulted, the imposition that Mgr Abbioso, assistant Archbishop of Pistoja and the Grand Duke's ambassador in Venice, had performed by laying his hands on her belly; none of these had produced more than the symptoms of pregnancy.

Some of the things that Donna Eleonora was told about Don Vincenzo were Greek to her, but her cousin, Virginio Orsini di Bracciano, fourteen years old, acted as interpreter. This boy, whom the Grand Duke loved as much as the Cardinal, was the image of their sister Isabella, who had been strangled out of jealousy by her husband, a prince attendant on the pontifical throne.

On the sly, the Princess and her young cousin studied the pictures, tapestries, and statues collected by the Grand Duke for the Pitti Palace and the Uffizi Gallery. Michelangelo's instructive statue of David was at the Piazza della Signoría, while in the Grand Duchess's very antechamber, beside the Pope's cup, was to be seen the no-less-eloquent shape of the Greek bronze Idolino, the gift of the Duchess of Urbino. The mythical nudes on the canvases stirred the Princess, as similar works of art had stirred Sister Maura Lucenia. The tapestries of the Months, woven in Florence from cartoons by the Flemish masters, depicted lords and menservants with well-stuffed hose—men's fashions in Tuscany were less obtrusive.

What Donna Eleonora could not understand, despite Virginio's help, was the meaning of the word 'impotence.' She unbosomed herself to the family confessor, Fr Maranta, a Dominican. Her question astonished him, but she said she had the right to know what this infirmity was that the Prince of Mantua was suspected of. Fr Maranta, after reflecting for some time, thought it possible to give her the information in the words of one of the Fathers of the Church.

Unfortunately, he discovered, none of them had dealt with impotence. St Basil had, on the other hand, written about eunuchs; the Dominican supposed that their amorous endeavours, so energetically described by this scholar of the Greek Church, more or less corresponded to those of the impotent. But since this description figured in a book that Cardinal Farnese had quoted at the second Consistory, he hesitated to make such a choice. Besides, agents of the Farneses, encouraged by the fiasco at Ferrara, were busy spreading the rumour that the Prince was castrated. Thinking it over, Fr Maranta came to the conclusion that eunuchs did not come so badly out of the passage in *The Integrity of Virgins;* St Basil declared them to be capable of something, and this could do away with the Princess' prejudices. The friar translated for her the following lines:

'Just as the bull that strikes with its horns, and from which the horns are removed, does not become a horse through the loss of its horns, but remains a bull, though it no longer has horns; in the same way, the male whose genitals are removed does not become a female through the loss of his genitals, but remains a male, though he no longer has genitals. And just as the bull, when its horns are removed, still strikes with its horns, for it strikes with the part of its head where it had been provided with horns; in the same way, the male whose genitals are removed is still a male, by virtue of his male desires, though he no longer has genitals.'

12

On February 19, while the Grand Duke and Grand Duchess were in Leghorn, Princess

Anna died of a bleeding from the nose. Donna Eleonora, distracted by this sudden death, was the only one at her favourite sister's bedside and supervised the funeral singlehanded.

On the road to the church of St Lawrence, the burial procession passed Secretary of State Donati, Don Guglielmo's new envoy. He had come to Florence, on this melancholy day, to settle the details of the test by congress. Not being superstitious, he did not take the encounter as a bad omen.

Mgr Capilupi and Don Carlo Gonzaga welcomed him to the house of the knight Vinta. This personage, formerly ambassador in Vienna and (with the knight Serguidi) the Grand Duke's chief minister, had been appointed to conduct negotiations with the Mantuan plenipotentiary. He was also charged with the task of finding a desirable victim for Don Vincenzo, taking her to Venice, where the altar would be set up, and examining the sacrificial knife.

Vinta's first task was to tour the Florentine foundling hospitals. The chief physician at the palace, Master Cappelli, joined him in the quest. Neither the St Innocent orphanage, nor the Waifs and Strays of St Nicholas, nor those of St Mary of the Angels, yielded, from among their sad regiments, the female they dreamed of. 'All these girls are ugly and spotty, with such poor skin that they make you sick,' wrote the knight to the Grand Duke. However, at the Piety orphanage, run by the Ursulines, two girls were 'rather pleasing'; but they were rather more than twenty, and the Grand Duke wanted Don Vincenzo's partner to be the same age as Donna Eleonora. So these two were 'bespoken, but not hired.'

During this search, Donati did not leave Vinta's house. The Medicis had arranged for him to stay hidden, so that it should not be thought that the marriage was settled. They were deluded by their love of secrecy. His presence in the city was notorious, and a member of the Accademia della Crusca dedicated a sonnet to him.

Donati had brought with him a memorandum, drawn up by the Duke and his son along the lines of the one agreed to in Ferrara. Knowing that the Medicis liked to negotiate 'in the form of a lawsuit,' the Gonzagas put forward their conditions for the heroine of the test—the conditions which scarcely seemed necessary. She must 'have a beautiful face,' be appetizing, refuse nothing, 'have no impediment,' and be to the liking of Donati, who knew the Prince's tastes.

The memorandum also specified that the Mantuan representative would visit Donna Eleonora, so that he might confirm to Don Vincenzo 'her renowned virtues and graces.' Vinta recalled the sad event which had bereaved the Princess, and which rendered her unable to see anyone. Besides, she had just rejoined the court at Leghorn, with Don Carlo and Master Cappelli. It would be perfectly fair if the Secretary caught a glimpse of her on her return, when she passed by in a coach.

The second day after the burial, the knight sent word to the Grand Duke that they were in process of 'cleaning and smartening up' one of the girls 'bespoken' at the Piety orphanage. For this operation a whole day was required, if not two. He 'was dressing her only in a sheet until she was approved of' and, as a measure of precaution, was beginning to get the other one cleaned up. What disturbed him a little was that Donati was insisting on the first of the conditions: 'The noble Prince insists on a beautiful face before anything else; so far as the rest is concerned, he would not look so closely.' But the girls he had 'bespoken' were 'tasty morsels rather than beauties.' Where could he go to find better?

A courier brought the knight a letter from Minister Serguidi. The Grand Duke, aware of 'the unattractiveness of the two bespoken girls,' instructed him to choose, from the same orphanage, an orphan called Giulia, 'who has a beautiful face and noble manners.'

The knight smiled at this errand; it had been suggested by the physician, in agreement with him. He had good enough eyes, and was enough of a courtier, to have noticed the beautiful face and noble manners of the orphan called Giulia. But he had not had the audacity to suggest that she be chosen, for she was a bastard of the Albizzis, an illustrious Florentine family connected with the Medicis. An Albizzi had married an uncle of Lorenzo the Magnificent; an Albizzi boy had been the darling of Pope Leo x, who had made him a prelate. An Albizzi had been the mistress of Cosimo i, and had borne him a son, whom he had legitima-

133

tized. An Albizzi was majordomo to the
Grand Duke. The Abbess of St Paul the
Greater, the Grand Duchess' friend, was an
Albizzi. For these various reasons, Serguidi rec-
ommended that neither Donati nor the Gon-
zagas must ever discover this girl's origin.

The knight received a note informing him
that Napoleone Cambi, Depositary General,
would pay him the necessary sum for the orphan's clothing and the journey to Venice, but
that everything must be done 'as economically
as possible.'

13

While the Ursuline nuns at the Piety orphanage, secure from censure, decked out the beautiful Giulia, the knight talked things over with
his guest. Each was trying to worm out the
other's secrets, and claiming that the party he
represented was the more important. One
boasted of the great princes who aspired to
Donna Eleonora's hand; the other, the great
princesses who were offered to Don Vincenzo.

The Mantuan said his Prince had preferred Donna Leonora to anyone else, because—in confidence—he was 'enamoured' of her. The Florentine could not bring himself to express Donna Eleonora's platonic feelings, but made the most of her parents' 'amiable sincerity.'

He also gave an account of her charms. Serguidi had warned him to decline a meeting between the Secretary and the Princess; still dejected about the loss of her sister, she would not do herself justice. If Donati were not satisfied with what Vinta had told him, all he need do was go to the Grand Duke's room in the Uffizi Gallery, where he would see a charming portrait of her by Bronzino.

The test by congress remained the central point of their discussions. Donati, as Don Vincenzo's former tutor and physician, vouched for his virility, as Don Cesare had done. 'The noble Prince,' he said, 'would not be so foolish as to go into a gallop if his charger were broken-winded.' What was more, 'it was not only a question of his virility, but of his honour.' That was why he must not be sent 'bound hand and foot' into such a serious and even essential test, but must have free play.

The knight looked at his opposite number in amazement. Had not Mgr Capilupi, on behalf of Don Guglielmo, signed the terms of 'one night, in three attempts'? Had the Gonzagas acquiesced only to go back on their word? Had they pretended to agree, in order to compel the Medicis to submit to their intentions? At the very moment of crossing swords, here they were returning to 'the Ferrara question.'

Donati protested that his journey to Florence proved their desire to settle the matter, but that they were hoping for the softening of a Draconian clause. Yes, they had accepted and would continue to accept the terms of one night, in three attempts. But the Prince, although he did not doubt that he would get home 'with the very first thrust,' was afraid of finding himself cooled off by the thought of some sort of time limit. Vinta, who loved proverbs, knew that, according to Tuscan folklore, *il conno non vuol pensieri*—'Priapus does not want you to think.'

Don Vincenzo wanted to show his mettle, not in one night, but in three. He wanted to be able to 'go out, take a walk, get some fresh air, before going back for another tilt.' Freed from the hourglass, he would be freed also from apprehension and would recover his powers. But Vinta would not commit himself about the possibility of modifying what the Holy Father himself had thought to be reasonable.

He took the opportunity to question Donati about the Prince's person. The Secretary stated positively that it was neither monstrously huge nor monstrously tiny. All the same, its size was considerable, and it 'required more effort than another man's to do its duty.' The knight hastened to reassure the Grand Duke by sending him these details. And he drew this moral: 'What does size matter? The essential thing is to pierce and go in.'

14

On February 22 the lovely Giulia, escorted by a matron and two lay sisters, left the orphanage to go to Vinta's house. Heaven had given her 'the face of an angel,' and baths had freshened up her beauty. She was 'serious, unassuming, modest.' Although she was twenty, she seemed as young as Princess Eleonora. The knight saw an advantage in these few extra years: 'her membranes would be harder.' She was dressed in black, but he had had made for her 'a blue dress in Perpignan cloth, a cloak with sleeves, a white linen collaret, and other knick-knacks.' In spite of his thriftiness, and the advice he had been given to economize, the knight considered that, even if she were not acceptable, she ought to be given to someone as a present, 'for the love of God.'

The two lay sisters stayed in the antechamber. The lovely Giulia and the matron went into a small, candle-lit room. The matron undressed the young woman, and she was then examined and palpated by Master Cappelli, who had come from Leghorn at full speed. The knight observed the details of the examination and palpation. Then he went back to the Piety orphanage with the beauty and her companions.

He had not revealed to her why she had been dressed up. But the Mother Superior of the Ursulines was no less interested than the Abbess of St Paul in the fate of Donna Eleonora, and it was possible that she had spoken to her inmate. She had told the knight of her joy in obeying Gregory XIII, who had enriched the community with privileges; and in being of service to the Prince, whose cousin, Fr Francesco Gonzaga, had revised their rules. Vinta, forgetting the Albizzi family, described to the Grand Duke the breast, croup, and thoroughbred bearing of 'the filly that he has to cover.' This metaphor complemented Donati's one about the Prince's 'charger.'

As to the conditions of the 'covering,' the Grand Duke saw as clearly as his representative what the Mantuans were aiming at. He sent Don Carlo to Florence to chide Don Guglielmo's Secretary. But he showed his good will by proposing, in place of one night, 'twenty-four hours in succession.' When this was agreed, he would communicate certain 'special instructions.' He had already made clear what was, to his mind, 'the essential thing'—'to be certain of the girandolas.'

How could he not have been anxious about something which appeared on the Medici coat-of-arms? The people called the Medici heraldic besants 'balls.' 'Forward, balls!' was the Tuscan troops' battle cry. 'Balls, balls!' had been the cry of joy in Rome when the election of the Medici Popes Leo x and Clement vii was announced. 'Balls, balls!' was the greeting of the Florentines when the Grand Duke, his brother the Cardinal Senior Deacon, and their cousin the Archbishop passed by. The glory of the 'balls' was extolled in a carnival song. But Vinta had quoted to the Grand Duke the proverb: 'All balls are not round, and all spindles are not straight.'

Donati went on quibbling. He wanted the twenty-four hours to be 'split.' The knight replied that the Grand Duke's forbearance was at an end, and that it would be useless, even dangerous, to make any further appeal to him. On the advice of his two countrymen, the Mantuan gave in.

The lovely Giulia was brought to Vinta's house once more. Helped by Master Cappelli, Donati examined her. He carefully noted 'that she had no impediment.' He would have preferred her to be a little younger, but he was 'satisfied' with her. She was pronounced 'suitable for the test.' Don Carlo and Mgr Capilupi, who arrived soon afterwards, signified their assent.

The knight was considering how he could prevent them from repudiating their agreement at a later stage. If the Mantuans wanted to resort to subterfuge, might they not allege that the girl produced in Venice was not the one they had examined in Florence? Don Guglielmo's minister, asked to provide a certificate of identity, replied that he attested his agreement, in the presence of his two fellow Mantuans and his medical colleague, Master Cappelli. He was sure that the Prince would like the girl. It only remained to tell her 'what she would have to do.'

The knight reported his success to the Grand Duke. He was ready to strike camp with his 'troop.' He asked whether he should address Don Vincenzo as 'Highness.'

On everyone's behalf, Serguidi wrote back congratulating him on his 'discretion.' The chief surgeon, Master Galletti, was taking the place of Master Cappelli, who was being kept in Leghorn. The knight was permitted to call the Prince 'your Highness,' but only in words, not in writing, until the marriage had taken place. The special instructions must be initialled by Donati. The Grand Duchess had written them out herself, at the Grand Duke's dictation; they were a more detailed version of the clauses governing the Ferrara test, which had gone off at half cock.

The special instructions began by repeating that 'the test would take place within twenty-four consecutive hours.' The room would be 'chosen, made ready, and guarded by the representatives of his Most Serene Highness.' 'The noble Prince must go in alone, undressed, a night robe over his nightshirt.' He must let them verify that 'he had only his natural instruments, and that he was properly developed, well-proportioned, and complete.' 'His Most Serene Highness's minister must see him with his eyes, and touch him with his hand, while he is at work.' Lastly—since Easter was not far off—the test must not be held during Holy Week.

The question of seeing and touching had been debated at length by the two ministers. To the Grand Duke this was a matter of prime importance, and he had refused to abandon it. In vain did Donati point out that, in Ferrara, this task had not been entrusted to Ambassador Urbani, but to a prince, Don Cesare d'Este. Vinta was a minister; moreover he was provisionally responsible for State secrets. He thus enjoyed a status which an ordinary Knight of St Stephen, or even an ambassador, could not have claimed.

On the other hand, it was agreed that within the twenty-four hours the Prince would be free to make several attempts, until his work was accomplished. The knight added this marginal note for form's sake. For his part, he specified that he intended 'to keep a register, and note the comings and goings.' He did not add that the Grand Duke, in extending the number of hours, was continuing to limit the number of attempts.

The special instructions were signed by the two ministers on February 25, at three o'clock in the morning. A copy was immediately sent off to Mantua.

Mgr Capilupi, Donati, and Don Carlo set out next day, after worshipping the relics of St Mary of the Flower.

Part Four

1

The birth of a grandson, though it slightly delayed the knight, seemed a good omen. On March 1, he set out with Master Galletti. With them were the beautiful Giulia and the two matrons, travelling in a litter with drawn curtains. The two lay sisters were left behind. The escort consisted of Captain Digni and four servants.

'To spare the ladies,' their pace was slow, and they stopped that evening in Firenzuola. They were still in Tuscany and, though Vinta had 'changed his style of dress' and left off his cross of St Stephen, he was afraid of being recognized. He had given orders that questioners should be told that he was going to Germany with the daughter of Captain Freuberger, the former commander of Grand Duke Cosimo's halberdiers. He remembered the Abbot of

Prato, surnamed Firenzuola after his birth-place, who would have made the lovely Giulia the subject of one of his ribald tales. At least one other author and poet of the same stamp, Lasca, had dropped dead in Florence, a few hours before Princess Anna, while laughing at the latest details of the story.

Next day the travellers came to Bologna, whose walls they skirted. Cardinal Cesi was still keeping vigil in Rome, or else they would have sought his blessing. His assistant, Mgr Frangipani, Bishop of Nazareth, sent them his good wishes, which they received at 'the first inn beyond the gate, on the road to Mantua.' They stayed the next night at Bomporto. This was not the shortest route, but it was 'the most agreeable and the safest.' It had been worked out in agreement with the Mantuans, so that they would not have to cross Ferrarese terri-tory.

On Sunday, March 4, they heard mass in the abbey of St Benedict, on the bank of the Po— the men in the church, the lovely Giulia and the matron in a gallery, behind a grating. They were on Mantuan territory, but Don Gugli-elmo respected their incognito. The monks showed them some paintings by Giulio Romano, more seemly than those at the Palazzo del Té; and they venerated the remains of the Grand Countess Matilda, donatrix of the patrimony of St Peter.

Before long, the little caravan dismounted to sail down the Po to the Adriatic. But the wind was unfavourable, and it was a stormy voyage. They put in at Chioggia, 'for the sake of the ladies,' who were in a bad way and had to be revived. For the crossing, the knight chartered a felucca with eight oarsmen, and was glad he had done so. The wind and the rain did not let up for a minute. The sea was so heavy that they had to take off the awning. It was not excessive to have these eight 'strong and skilled' men.

'Greatly fatigued,' they landed in Venice just before midnight on Wednesday, March 7—two days late for the rendezvous. The lovely Giulia had suffered on board 'the Po boat,' and still more on board the Adriatic one. Vinta was even afraid that this young woman, 'who had never left her room,' would not reach Venice alive. She had 'almost lost her appetite.' But the knight suspected that this might also be caused 'by her joy at her good fortune.' For he had by now officially told her what high destiny was hers for an interval of twenty-four hours; how she was privileged to make love without sinning; and what her reward would be.

Don Vincenzo, Don Carlo, and Donati had left Mantua on March 3. On the previous evening, Secretary Gabbioneta had come back from Rome, where, he said, the Fathers in the purple were waiting impatiently 'for news of the noble Prince's person.' He had left behind Mgr Zibramonti, who had not yet received the Bull for a new erection, and who was no less impatient for news from Mantua. Gabbioneta sent him word that their young master was going to 'try his strength in single combat.' He ended his letter with the cry: 'May God grant us victory!'

The Mantuans had a worse journey than the Florentines. It reminded Donati of his unfortunate encounter on the day he arrived in Florence. To make it seem that this was an ordinary voyage, Don Vincenzo had borrowed the Mantuan State barge, and this solid ship saved their lives. On the Po, a windmill sail, torn off by a gust of wind, came crashing down and all but capsized them. Another followed it soon afterwards, increasing the damage. 'Everyone shouted "Jesus! Jesus!," and the noble Prince was getting ready to swim for it,' wrote Ambassador Calzoni after hearing the story of this voyage. Nor was this all: in Stellata, a fief of Don Alfonso's, the boat carrying Don Carlo's servants was held up by bandits and subjected to a harquebusade—a greeting from the Estes or the Farneses. Nevertheless, the Mantuans, treated more kindly by the Adriatic than by the Po, landed in Venice on Monday, March 5, at ten o'clock in the evening, precisely the appointed time. Not seeing the Florentines on the 6th or 7th, they feared that 'something sinister' had occurred.

Vinta refrained from visiting two personages well known for their love of intrigue: the Grand Duke's ambassador, Mgr Abbioso, Coadjutor to the Bishop of Pistoja, and Count Vittore Cappello, the Grand Duchess' brother. Instead he went to visit Master Guglielmo, the Medicis' 'factor,' who was completely trustworthy, and whose comfortable, secluded house made an ideal setting for an amatory adventure. Alas! 'Master Guglielmo was on his deathbed. As Vinta, Surgeon Galletti, Captain

Digni, the beautiful Giulia, and their servants went through the gates, extreme unction was being administered to him.

This new funeral disturbed the knight more than the burial of Princess Anna had disturbed Donati. The happy portent of his grandson's birth was wiped out. He wondered whether it was seemly to have a licentious scene, even one approved of by the Holy Father, played in the shadow of death. He was inclined to turn back and look for another lodging. But Master Guglielmo's housekeeper—Mgr Abbioso's former wetnurse—told him that everything was ready for him and his retinue. He decided to stay. Just as Urbani had sworn the widow Ligorio, he swore the nurse to secrecy.

2

After installing the lovely Giulia, eating a morsel of food, and praying at Master Guglielmo's bedside, Vinta made his way to the Gonzaga palace on the Grand Canal. Despite the late hour, he had sent word of his arrival to Donati, who joined him at once. The two Secretaries of State had been making inroads into their sleep ever since they had been devising a road to glory for the Prince. They described their odysseys to each other, trembled at the dangers they had escaped from, and blessed Heaven for bringing them into port. At two in the morning Don Vincenzo, who had come back with Don Carlo, burst in.

This was the first time the knight had set eyes on him. He kissed his hand, addressed him as 'your Highness,' and greeted him on behalf of the Medicis. Then he delivered a little speech designed to recall, as if it needed recalling, why the four of them were there: it was because of 'certain rumours spread, confidently and in detail, by evil-intentioned persons. The Grand Duke and Grand Duchess were convinced that these rumours were false, but felt compelled to clear the matter up, to put their consciences at rest and relieve their souls.' Their 'burning desire to have the noble Prince as a son-in-law, and to forge such a beautiful link between their two houses' had been an incentive to them. They thanked him for having so generously agreed to this test, and asked him to take it fairly, 'in order to respond to the honesty of their intentions.' The knight took the liberty of adding, in his own name, that 'since he had on his shoulders the burden of the undertaking,' he entreated 'H.H. to help him give his masters as good service as he wished to give the girl.' He must therefore 'reveal the naked truth, for the slightest suspicion would spoil the entire structure.'

The Prince's first words were 'of respect for their Most Serene Highnesses.' He went on to declare that he had 'resolved to take this test in order to satisfy them, though he did not trouble himself about tittle-tattle.' He returned, in different words, to Donati's argument about his 'charger.' 'I should not have been so rash, nor so careless of my peace of mind,' he said, 'as to want to marry a woman, especially this woman, without being able to hope for the fruits that are expected from marriage. But it is not our fault if some people are foolish and spiteful.' He concluded with words that fell pleasingly on Vinta's ear and showed his respect for the agreement: 'Since honour is more precious to me than life, I, like yourself, do not want the slightest suspicion to remain. That is why your Lordship will be free to see and to touch.' Don Carlo referred to the faith of St Thomas Aquinas, and the knight quoted the Florentine saying: 'It is good to see and better to touch.'

Don Vincenzo, too, would have liked to see and touch; he could have taken possession of his 'filly' there and then. His charger, which had been prancing for nearly a week, galloped better in the early morning. He had not specified this in his memorandum, because he had never imagined that they would make him perform before witnesses. Donati, having had the honour of guiding his pupil's first steps in love-making, had instilled into him the old adage that the body is fittest for this exercise around cockcrow. The knight told the Prince that the twenty-four hours could begin whenever he liked, but that he would have to hopple his charger for a short while: Master Guglielmo was dying, and the lovely Giulia had started her period on the 5th. The Prince burst out laughing at so many mishaps. They would make a Lenten oblation, he said.

3

When the knight awoke, he was told that Master Guglielmo was still breathing, that Master Galletti was down with fever, and that the lovely Giulia's period was taking its normal course.

The room in which the virgin and the matron were lodged communicated with Vinta's and with a balcony bordering on the Grand Canal. The door of this balcony, he wrote to the Grand Duke, was 'fastened on the inside by a strong lock of which he had the key.' The two windows that let air into the room were protected by a double row of bars. Finally, Captain Digni was stationed 'day and night underneath these two windows, and never loses sight of the balcony.' Vinta had good reason to claim that he was watching over the lovely Giulia 'as if she were his own sister.'

That afternoon Carlo Gonzaga and Donati came to greet him. They asked how the period was going, and whether Master Guglielmo was dead yet. Could not the Prince at least come and take a look at his partner? The knight begged them to be patient: his host's death was imminent, and he had ordered the body to be taken away without delay. He accepted the Prince's invitation to go for a gondola trip.

Don Vincenzo said he was glad 'to make himself acquainted with him and see him better than by candlelight.' Vinta, in turn, could examine the Prince in comfort, so that he could describe him to Don Francesco: 'The noble Prince seems handsome to me; he is a little taller than I am; he has firm flesh, fair hair, which he wears rather long, a little down on his upper lip, an elegant figure. His movements are lively. If the parts that are hidden, and the test that is to be made of them, come up to the outward appearance, I am convinced that your Most Serene Highness will be well satisfied with him.' He dressed in the French style, was passionately fond of hunting, especially boar hunting, and 'was dying to go hunting in Tuscany, of which he had heard wonders.' He spoke of the marriage as of something settled, and of the test as something whose outcome was not in doubt. The knight acknowledged his 'discernment and maturity' in spite of 'his youthful impetuousness.'

That morning, the Prince told Vinta, the Grand Duchess' brother had informed him of 'the arrival, on his account, of the Grand Duke's men and a young women.' Don Vincenzo had pretended to know nothing about it. He was astonished that the news had leaked out so quickly, and swore that it was not the fault of the Gonzaga palace. The knight replied that it was not his fault, either. They promised each other to give stricter orders than ever about secrecy.

Vinta stepped out of the gondola just in time to offer up a prayer for Master Guglielmo, whose coffin lid was being nailed down. He would have liked to be present at the funeral of this faithful servant of the Grand Duke, but he was under orders to remain strictly incognito. He had to get rid of a notary, who was handling the formalities, and a servant of Mgr Abbioso's, who came to ask 'who these Florentine gentlemen were that had brought a girl with them.'

While the little house was being tidied up for the Prince, the knight, mindful of all his master's interests, locked up the dead man's papers. He intended to pass them over to Master Abbioso, the ambassador's cousin, but 'a man of property, and level-headed,' to whom he would entrust the agency until the Grand Duke filled the post. On the other hand, he would send the funds to Florence, in chests properly bound and sealed.

Don Vincenzo, flanked by Carlo Gonzaga and Donati, presented himself at half past one in the morning. He saw the beauty, was delighted, thanked Donati and Vinta for their choice, and 'manifested a strong desire to begin the test straight away.' But Donati established that 'the region was still humid.'

On Friday, March 9, Donati came to see if there was any change, but there was none. He told the knight that he would hand two hundred crowns to the lovely Giulia 'in the event of the test succeeding and not otherwise.' Vinta replied, with some pride, that such conditional generosity would be superfluous; the Grand Duke had decided to find the girl a husband and dower her, 'without the noble Duke and the noble Prince having a hand in the matter.' 'If they wish to offer her something, why prevent them?' asked Donati. The knight told him not to be in such a hurry; it was not necessary to 'copy the Genoese nuns, who celebrate Easter on Palm Sunday.'

That evening, ahead of schedule, the Prince reappeared, crying that his charger was rearing up. 'He made a pretence of violating the girl, but she showed her good education by a seemly resistance.' Master Galletti, who had got over his fever, soothed the Prince's fever by confirming that 'the region was not yet completely dry.' And the knight added that they ought to respect the holy day of Friday.

4

Don Vincenzo did not present himself again until Sunday, March 11, at four o'clock in the morning. The 'region' was in a suitable condition: the lovely Giulia 'had been washed and made alluring from head to foot, and would have brought a block of marble to life.' Schooled by Vinta, coached by the matron, she showed herself 'as eager to give herself to H.H.

as to obey your Most Serene Highnesses.' The Prince was escorted only by the captain of his guards, his cousin Guido Gonzaga.

The latter had brought a bundle containing the 'night robe,' a pair of new sheets, and a clean nightshirt. Mgr Abbioso's nurse had sent a packed meal; she had tried to choose foods that would stimulate love, but her choice had been circumscribed by the austerity proper to the fourth Sunday in Lent. The matron, Don Guido, and Vinta remade the bed with the new sheets. The virgin undressed behind a folding screen, and the Prince in full view. As required by the Grand Duke and Grand Duchess, he showed the knight that 'his instruments were properly developed, well-proportioned, and complete.' This simple examination proved that the Farneses had lied in their teeth when they called his person 'wretched and shrunken' or bereft of girandolas. On the other hand, its size in repose somewhat disappointed the knight; it did not justify the opposite claim, which Donati had in fact repudiated.

Don Vincenzo asked the knight to help him on with his clean nightshirt and so establish that 'he had only his natural instruments with him.' Then he slipped between the sheets. The knight reminded him that he awaited his summons for the supplementary verification. As he shut the door, he said to himself that he would reopen it for the most extraordinary duty ever performed by a minister and ex-ambassador. He noted the time in his register and threw himself, fully dressed, on his bed. The cousin was already asleep, but Vinta did not even begin to feel sleepy.

The Prince was in bed with the girl for four and a half hours. Vinta grew more and more astonished at the silence from the next room. His astonishment at last turned into despair. He murmured a proverb: 'To wait for someone who does not come, to be devoted to someone whom one cannot serve, to be two in a bed without enjoying it: these are the three deadliest things in the world.' He glued his ear to the door. Don Vincenzo was snoring. 'A sleeping man catches no fish,' he thought, and he finished off the proverb: 'A sleeping fish catches nothing.' He thought sadly of the letter from Florence telling him that his grandson, born before his departure, 'had gone to heaven.'

Suddenly, he felt happier. The bells for seven o'clock mass rang out like a trumpet call. The test bed creaked joyfully. Vinta said a prayer. He remembered that it was *Laetare* Sunday, when the Pope blessed the Golden Rose.

His musings were interrupted by hurried footsteps. The Prince, ghastly pale, loomed up in the doorway. He was clutching his belly with both hands and groaning: 'Oh, knight, knight! I am terribly ill!' Vinta and Don Guido ran to help him sit down. He was suffering from violent pains in the stomach; the knight was thankful that he had not sent in the nurse's packed meal. Don Vincenzo was subject to this ailment, especially in Venice. 'He had eaten too much Lenten food, particularly oysters.' He had felt off colour during the day, and this had made him late; but he had been hoping for a miracle.

The Prince did not want to disturb Donati, and was satisfied with the help of Master Galletti, who applied hot cloths to his abdomen. He decided to leave, though he was not much better; he would give himself a sweet-almond oil clyster, 'which generally cured him.' He expected to return that evening to make up for lost time. The two Florentines saw him to his gondola. He floated off, supported by Don Guido and vomiting into the canal.

The knight, with the surgeon on his heels, dashed back to his pupil. He had not dared to question the Prince, and was burning with impatience to know what had happened.

'I am just as I was,' said the lovely Giulia, who looked quite crestfallen. 'The noble Prince kissed my lips, stroked my neck, ran his hands over my body, and felt my fig. Then he dropped off to sleep, with his face close to mine. He woke up a few minutes before seven o'clock, pressed me in his arms, lay on me without anything happening, and climbed off again. Then he started trembling so violently that he shook the bed, while the bells were ringing for mass. Then he started moaning and went out of the room.'

When the knight told her that the Prince 'would do this evening what he could not do this morning,' she burst out laughing and cried: 'What do you want me to do? I didn't even feel his person. Don't talk to me about *that* any more!'

Vinta apologized for these words when he

reported them to the Grand Duke: 'The poor little thing! After the water was almost in her mouth she had to remain thirsty.' He defended the lovely Giulia, but he did not believe in the bright prospect he had held out to her. He was now doubtful about Don Vincenzo's sincerity, and he expressed himself on the subject with his customary bluntness:

'I am dumbfounded at such a lack of virility in such a well-developed young man, and at his folly, and his family's folly, in submitting to a test for which he is manifestly unfit. Does he think we cannot tell a cow from a bull? Really, there never has been and never will be anyone so foolish as he is.'

5

The bells, on that *Laetare* Sunday which had begun so badly, seemed to be ringing the knell of Don Vincenzo's marriage to Donna Eleonora. The knight, no less carefully disguised than Urbani had been in Ferrara, went sadly to the Church of St Mary of the Miracles for mass. The miracle to be desired for the prince was not the kind one could ask heaven to grant.

Carlo Gonzaga, Donati, and Vinta held a discussion, worthy of the two Consistories, at the late Master Guglielmo's house. His register in his hand, the knight read out in a loud voice the statement he had taken down, counter-signed by Master Galletti and the matron. After which he did not mince words with his two visitors. 'In view of the noble Prince's frigidity,' they had better take leave of each other and spare themselves the trouble of new setbacks. It could be announced that the agree-ment was cancelled because of illness.

The Secretary replied that they had not yet, thank God, been driven to that extremity. He spoke of the mishap from a medical point of view. He explained that lack of exercise in Venice, as well as the Venetian food, had made the Prince unwell. He recalled what he had said about the Prince's person, and asked the knight if he did not agree that it was the oppo-site of the kind an impotent man would have.

Vinta shook his head. 'Even if, in the second bout, the noble Prince were seen and touched in action, this demonstration would no longer satisfy their Most Serene Highnesses; the success would have been preceded by too much failure.' Donati was unmoved; according to the agreement, the Prince had the right to try his luck several times during the twenty-four hours—three times, according to the original conditions. Vinta was forced to acknowledge this, but he added that 'if the second attempt resembled the first, he did not know whether he would give the signal for a third.' Though Donati protested, Carlo Gonzaga agreed with this opinion; he considered that another failure would, in point of fact, put Don Vincenzo *hors de combat*. Whereupon the Mantuans withdrew, 'looking as ill as the noble Prince.'

Donati reacted swiftly, nevertheless. He sent the knight a memorandum cancelling Don Carlo's concession and claiming the right to two attempts in the forthcoming twenty-one hours. Don Vincenzo's condition, he added, had the effect of adjourning the test *sine die*. While pretending to keep to the letter of the agreement, he was turning the circumstances to account. He had in fact succeeded in 'splitting' the twenty-four-hour period.

Everything now depended on the Gonzaga palace. The Prince, having got over his colic, was reputed to have a fever. 'I suspect,' wrote the knight, 'that they are trying to revive his spirits by making him take a few days' rest. This is going to cause me a great deal of anxiety and a great deal of expense, for living in Venice is shockingly dear.'

Leaving Donati to gain time with Vinta, Carlo Gonzaga sent Don Guglielmo his impressions. He told him how he had begged the Prince, for the honour of the family, not to persevere in the test without express instructions from Mantua. He recapitulated the omens of failure: Donati's arrival in Florence on a day of mourning; the fall of the two windmill sails on the State barge; the harquebus shots at the servants' boat; the death of the Grand Duke's agent; the lovely Giulia's period; the stomach pains that had prostrated the Prince; the news that Vinta's grandson had gone to heaven. 'All this,' he concluded, 'reflects a secret judgment of God, and condemns the test.' Donati himself, infected by his pessimism, admitted to the Duke that their project was repugnant to 'the divine will.' He saw yet another sign in the

Prince's mood; hitherto he had been 'full of ardour and desire,' but now he was 'lying dejectedly on his bed.' The Minister took Don Carlo's advice and asked for instructions before the two final attempts. He finished his letter with this call, an echo of Gabbioneta's cry to Mgr Zibramonti: 'May God help us!'

The Prince, too, made a confession to his father. He blamed fate. To kindle a hope, he suggested that 'instead of going on with the Florence match, we should discuss the Lorraine match with the Most Christian ambassador.'

And in fact, since the Prince's arrival in Venice, Hurault de Maisse had renewed his offer. To while away the two days before the Florentines reached Venice, Don Vincenzo, without the slightest qualm, had invited the French ambassador to come and see him. The ambassador had said 'how solid the Lorraine match was.' During the lovely Giulia's period, the Prince had thought about returning this visit, but Donati had made him postpone it. Now he was thinking about it again, as a way out of the Medici trap. Had not Hurault de Maisse said, only a short time ago, that France would not require him to pass any dishonourable test?

The Count of San Giorgio, captain general of the Duke's guards, brought the Prince Don Guglielmo's reply. It was resolutely negative: 'Your Highness has had enough embarrassment with Parma, and has enough at the moment with Florence, not to create still more with such a great sovereign as the King of France. In any case, you should not dream of such a thing until you have proved your virility beyond a shadow of doubt.'

Once more the Prince was put under the authority of Mgr Capilupi, whose fate it was to be involved in this canonical imbroglio to the very end. The historian of the St Bartholomew massacre defied the bandits and the tempests, and landed in Venice with this further message for the Prince from Don Guglielmo: 'If your Highness' impediment is really due to the stomach ache and not to inability, it is good that you should repeat the test, so as to finish off an act of such importance.'

Don Vincenzo was brought to bay. Hurault de Maisse sent him the despatch he had received from the Louvre palace. Stirred by so many rumours, France in turn was asking the Prince to dispel them. The Lorraine match might be as 'solid' as ever—but it now depended on incontestable proof of Mantuan solidity.

6

Donati had arranged with Vinta that the second attempt should be made on the evening of March 12. Now he cried off: 'The noble Prince still has a touch of fever. He is keeping to his room, and I cannot leave him. My kindest regards.' His kindest regards were not enough for the Grand Duke's Minister. 'The noble Prince's continued fever,' he replied by the same gondolier, 'breaks my heart, and I wish I could give him my own blood. I pray for his health, but time flies, and your Lordship will remember what we agreed. The matter must be settled urgently.'

A prisoner in the little house, Vinta explored Master Guglielmo's library. Who would have thought that this simple man—peace to his blessed soul!—would have collected so many bawdy books? His modesty had often dis-

guised them: *St Peter's Tears,* by the Venetian
Tansillo, a poem written for Paul IV, was
bound with the same author's obscene *Vin-
tager,* written for the same Pope's nephew. Pos-
sibly the licentious books that Churchmen
wrote were licensed by the Index Committee of
the College of Cardinals—books like the *Capitolo on the Oven,* in praise of sodomy, by the
Florentine Mgr de la Casa, Archbishop of Ben-
evento, and Venetian Cardinal Bembo's *Hymn
to Priapus.* A book by Aretino, *Capitoli to
Noblemen,* provided some timely reading matter: the poet related some rather indelicate tales
to Duke Frederico, Don Vincenzo's grandfather; and he described to Cosimo I, Donna
Eleonora's grandfather, how he had cured himself of the quartan ague—by tumbling his
maidservant. 'Would to God that was the noble
Prince's remedy, instead of clysters,' the knight
said to himself.

However, he had seen to it that the lovely
Giulia would still let herself be tumbled. A
note had informed him of Mgr Capilupi's arrival and Don Guglielmo's decision. He was
not surprised to see the Gonzagas remaining
faithful to the motto of one of their ancestors:

Frangar, non flectar—'I bend, but do not break.' Their scion, alas! seemed to find more favour with Consistories than with ladies. In spite of all the injunctions and promises about secrecy, repeated in every letter and every discussion, he had become the laughingstock of Venice. The gondoliers' jokes about him rivalled those of the Ferrarese fishwives.

For fear of irritating the Grand Duke, Mgr Abbioso did not dare to spy on the little house; but he felt less constraint at the Gonzaga palace. He was told that a waggish Frenchman— probably one of Hurault de Maisse's secretaries—had sent to the palace some satiric verses by Rémi Belleau, entitled *Blazon of Impotence.* They were not so pleasant for Don Vincenzo as the poem which Aretino had dedicated to his grandfather, Duke Frederico, and which was a pendant to the eulogy of the quartan ague, dedicated to Donna Eleonora's grandfather. Belleau wrote:

I am becalmed, disheartened,
Paralysed, broken-backed, flabby, washed out,
Heroic on the rampart, cowardly in the breach,
A dismounted gun, without primer or match,

A handle without a hammer, a mortar without
   a pestle,
A ship without a mast, a buckle without a catch,
A sinew that cannot be braced, a bow that
   cannot be bent.

Mgr Abbioso had laughed till the tears came.
Ambassador Urbani wrote to the Grand
Duke from Ferrara: 'It is known here that the
noble Prince is in Venice, and he is talked
about everywhere, as he was last month. . . . It
is said that the Florentine girl is very lovely.
. . . I gather that the test is not limited to one
night. Some say that it has already taken place,
successfully. But Don Alfonso has learned, from
Venice itself, that it was fixed for Sunday, then
Tuesday, then Wednesday. Each day's post
brings him fresh news. He has told me in confidence that Don Vincenzo is suffering from
fox evil. This rumour is no doubt being spread
deliberately.' 'Fox evil' was a way of saying the
French disease, which was being suggested as
the cause of the Prince's impotence.

At the Gonzaga palace they were beginning
to discern something more than a secret judgment of God. Don Carlo was the first to catch a

whiff of brimstone. He remembered that the question of evil spells had been discussed at the first Consistory. Mgr Capilupi kicked himself for not having thought of this first. Clearly, the Farneses had a sorcerer working for them. Appropriate action must be taken.

Dressed in surplice and stole, the Pope's Referendary performed the exorcism prescribed by ritual. The Prince, kneeling on his bed in his nightshirt, joined in the prayers. He felt no improvement. Mgr Capilupi was uneasy, and went to consult Fr Panigarola, who was preaching the Lenten sermons in Venice. Don Guglielmo's confessor recommended him to one of his colleagues, Fr Ippolito, who was renowned for the number of laces he had unknotted. This Franciscan handed him a cornet of consecrated lozenges which the devil had never yet withstood.

Victory! Thanks to the combined efforts of friar and prelate, Beelzebub fled, hanging his head; and the Prince raised his. Exultantly, Donati told the captain general of the Duke's guards: 'The flesh was tormenting H.H. all through the night of the 12th.' These torments brought nothing but rejoicing to the Gonzaga palace. Don Vincenzo invited the knight to come and admire his resurrection. But Vinta was avoiding personal contact with the Prince. If something fishy were going on, he did not want to be suspected of connivance. He replied that it would not be possible for him to leave the little house, but that he looked forward with good will to examining the Prince there.

On the 13th, during the day, Don Vincenzo left his room and went out in a gondola. He was dressed in Venetian costume, and wore a fur-lined cloak against the bad weather. He was 'so full of beans' that Donati wrote to the Count of San Giorgio: 'Tonight, God willing, I shall escort H.H. into the lists.' He was gratified to be acting as 'godfather,' since 'Mgr Capilupi cannot be there, and the noble and most illustrious Carlo is suffering from retention of urine.'

7

On Wednesday, March 14, at half past four in the morning, the Prince went once more to the little house. He had brought Donati and his barber, who carried the bundle. He was so good humoured, and looked so hale and hearty, that no one would have believed he had been ill. He wanted to make the bed himself, for he was afraid of bad luck if anyone else touched it. And soon the knight was drafting, at first in his head and then on paper, the incisive phrases of his letter to the Grand Duke— the most remarkable letter of his entire ministerial and diplomatic career:

'The girl being in bed, the noble Prince undressed in front of me, and I again saw him naked, before he put on his nightshirt. He exhibited himself without restraint, showed that he possessed only his natural weapons, and, at about five o'clock, lay down beside the girl. Half an hour later, he called out to me joyfully: "Knight, knight! come here, touch and feel!" And I, though not without some shame and deference, tried to slide my hand between their entwined thighs, but without success. The noble Prince raised himself, leaning on his elbow, and my hand went between their two bellies till I could touch H.H.'s pubic region and clasp his solid person, which the girl had inside her body. It was evident that she had it inside, for she was groaning, but not with pain alone. Then the noble Prince said: "Now you have touched and felt, and have informed yourself, leave me to my business." And he embraced the girl.'

Returning to Donati, who was quivering with impatience, Vinta described, 'in gestures and words,' the Prince's condition and his crossing of the Rubicon. They rendered thanks to God. They might sometimes have thanked him prematurely, but they had not implored him in vain. The slanders and the fears were swept away. They had provided Don Vincenzo with a wife, Donna Eleonora with a husband.

Forgetting sleep, they chatted in an undertone. They rejoiced at the creaking of the bed and the sighs in the next room. Vinta recalled Sunday's ominous silence, and the misleading noises that had accompanied the bells for seven o'clock mass. Donati, who now could notice only good omens, even discovered one in the date. March 14 was the feast day of St Matilda, whom the Mantuans confused with her namesake, the Grand Countess. That lady had bequeathed vast territories to the Holy See, and

Vinta, on his way to Venice, had venerated her tomb in the abbey of St Benedict. The Popes had neither canonized nor beatified her; but they so envied the Gonzagas her mortal remains that they had tried to steal them. Don Guglielmo had been afraid that Gregory XIII might demand them as his price of being so gracious about the Prince's person; this would have raised a thorny point of conscience.

Don Vincenzo did not open the door until two o'clock in the afternoon. He greeted his augurs jovially. He told them that he had 'broken three lances'—it would have been four, but he had dropped the first one in his haste. 'I did not call you till the second time,' he told the knight. 'I was in such a hurry that I missed my stroke.' His exploits had not tired him. Once more they observed him without clothes on, before the barber helped him on with his shirt, and they could verify, once again, that he had 'very fine flesh.' The windows were open, but he did not mind the cold.

Before he finished dressing, he summoned Master Galletti to corroborate Vinta's testimony. Don Francesco's surgeon noted that 'the person of H.H. was ordinary but well formed, as were the dependences, which he felt and weighed in his hand without observing anything abnormal.' The Prince declared that he 'had deserved well of the Most Serene Grand Duke, since, to please him, he had allowed a thorough study to be made of his anatomy.' Laughing, the knight replied that his own studies had been still more thorough, and that something would be missing from Master Galletti's certificate. 'It is up to him whether he sees me in the condition you saw me in,' retorted the Prince. 'I am always like that when I wake up.'

Donati seized the opportunity to enhance the prestige of the Gonzaga family, even of its sickly head. 'Your Highness,' he said, 'is a true son of your father, for the Most Serene Duke is in the same condition every morning.'

8

As soon as the Mantuans had left, the knight— more cheerful than on the previous occasion— hurried to the lovely Giulia. When he saw her in tears, he thought that she was weeping for her lost virginity. On the contrary, she was crying because she was still intact. She would not let them examine her; they must take her word for it. Master Galletti and Vinta, helped by the matron, held her down by main force; she was 'moist and gaping.' But the knight made it clear in his register that 'they were hardly competent judges,' either of them. Intimidated by the patient, they dared not expressly contradict her. The surgeon declared that it would take a physician to state positively that she was no longer a virgin; the matron, that it would take a nurse. Vinta was at his wits' end.

Giulia did, however, admit that the Prince had 'made four attempts at different times'; but she swore that he 'hardly went in.' When the knight protested that he had touched 'the noble Prince's person, hard and solid,' and that it was 'driven right in,' she still swore that she had felt nothing. He asked her why 'she was groaning'; she answered that 'H.H. had been hurting her, but without penetrating.' The sheets, which had been so spotlessly white when the Prince laid them, were stained with blood; this was because he had scratched her.

The knight 'examined her shift' and noticed some 'traces of semen'; Master Galletti found some on the sheets. She said that 'H.H., after rubbing himself against her, had finished himself off with his hand.' Unfortunately, they could not scrutinize the linen that Vinta had given the matron to be 'cleaned after the operation.' The lovely Giulia had been quite alone when she made her toilet, and had not been helped by a servant. How could they give her the lie when she called the test a wasted effort?

And yet, Vinta was well aware that the five fingers of his right hand had not grasped a phantom at five o'clock in the morning. But, before clearing the matter up, he was anxious to prevent the Mantuans from counting on a success which remained problematical. He sent a message begging them to hold up any courier until his arrival. Then he entered the new deposition in his register.

A second conference was held, with the two ministers, Guido Gonzaga, who had been composing his victory bulletin to Don Guglielmo, Carlo Gonzaga, who had been meditating, and Mgr Capilupi, who had been reciting his breviary. They did not disturb Don Vincenzo, who was busy entertaining his gentlemen in waiting with an account of his exploits. Vinta read the entry in his register and his hearers cried out in amazement. They called the lovely Giulia a slut, a tool of the Farneses. But the knight had guarded her too vigilantly to be altogether of their opinion.

By chance, the Prince entered the room; the gravity of this Areopagus astonished him. They told him what had happened. He laughed uproariously and said: 'I suspect that Signora Giulia is hankering after some more.' And everyone admired, not only his shrewdness, but also the elegance with which he dignified the lovely Giulia. He added: 'There is a charger that can see on the darkest night, although it is blind. After breaking open a door it would not bump against it without passing through.' Still in good humour, he went on: 'It seems to me, knight, that you were well able to judge whether the devil was in hell.' Vinta agreed with a smile, and Mgr Capilupi approved of a metaphor which paid homage to the exorcism. 'I, too, am hankering after some more,' said the Prince, more gaily than ever. 'I promise

myself to Signora Giulia for the coming night.'
Vinta commended this honourable resolve.

Don Vincenzo's counsellors, the protectors of
Mantuan honour and Mantuan hopes, were
less enthusiastic. His offer to put the devil back
into hell put them all back on the rack. Donati
declared that, whatever the she-devil said, the
test had surpassed all expectations; Mgr Capilupi implored the Prince to do nothing without
consulting Fr Panigarola and Fr Ippolito; Don
Guido besought him not to tempt God by an
adventure 'so pregnant with consequences';
Don Carlo pleaded with him not to risk his
reputation, 'under the eyes of the whole of
Italy, as one might say.' The Prince retorted
that, as matters stood, a little more or a little
less made no difference. And with that, he left
the room.

The knight increased their bewilderment
when he said that he would expect the Prince's
visit and that he was going to prepare Signora
Giulia for it. He had not yet written to Florence, and he asked his hosts not to write to
Mantua. Donati invoked the letter of the agreement. The Grand Duke and Grand Duchess
had appointed, not the girl, but their Minister

to judge whether the test were passed; the latter acknowledged that he had 'seen and touched' while the act was taking place. Vinta objected that the Grand Duke, in his special letters, had insisted on the girl's evidence. Don Carlo reminded him that she had spoken of four encounters; Mgr Capilupi, that the sheets and shift bore the proud marks of them. Don Guido, the honest captain of the guards, undertook to persuade Don Vincenzo to put up his sword.

Donati brought the debate to an end. Mantua would crown its champion and let Florence have it out with its championess.

9

The knight went back to the little house in his gondola. As he passed under the Bridge of Sighs he sighed himself and thought once more of the proverb about the Genoese nuns. The Gonzagas really did have a mania for chiming the bells ahead of the feast day.

A pleasant surprise was waiting for him.

Signora Giulia had confessed to the surgeon and the matron. The Prince was right: her denial was because she wanted to do it again. Now, there was no stopping her comments. He had 'gone in where he should have gone in'; she hoped 'that she was pregnant by him'; he was 'as smooth as milk, as hot as blood, as velvety as a fleece.' She was now a willing party to their examination of the damage she had suffered.

The knight was seized with one doubt. There were three canonical conditions for virility. Of *erectio* and *introductio* he was now sure; but could he be sure of *emissio,* which the Consistory had rather taken for granted? Although this detail was not mentioned in his instructions, it was his duty to be specific about it. The traces of semen which he had recorded in his register, and which had, with good reason, impressed Mgr Capilupi, could not fail to be interpreted in the Prince's favour. But—Vinta shuddered at the idea—who could say that they were not from Signora Giulia? Master Galletti allayed his scruples: 'Even if the girl did discharge, this semen was indeed the noble

Prince's.' He gave Vinta a 'demonstration' of the mechanism of the vessel.

There were many other things to be demonstrated. They proceeded to examine Signora Giulia methodically:

'Asked if she swore to tell the truth, she said yes!

'Had the noble Prince concealed an instrument made of iron or glass or any other substance, to enlarge or open her before possessing her?—No.

'Had he enlarged or opened her violently with his fingers?—No.

'Had he offered or given her jewels or money or anything else to make her speak as she did?—No.

'Had he threatened her with any kind of revenge if she spoke the truth?—No.

'Were her pubic region and the noble Prince's pubic region joined together?—Yes.

'How many times had he done it to her?— Three, for certain, and perhaps four.

'Had he penetrated on the first occasion?— He had not had time to do so.

'Was it on the second occasion that he called the knight Vinta in?—Yes.

'Had she felt the knight's hand clasp the noble Prince's person?—Yes.

'Did she at that time have it in her own person?—Yes.

'Had she groaned for shame or because he was hurting her?—Because he was hurting her.

'Was he hurting her inside or outside?'—Inside.

'Was he hard and solid?—Yes.

'While he was pushing, did he aim his person with his hand?—Yes.

'Did she touch it with her own hand?—No, although he wanted her to; but she refused out of modesty.

'Had he discharged into her?—Yes.

'Had she felt pleasure at that moment?—Yes.

'Would any girl who had to take a husband be satisfied with the noble Prince?—Yes, as far as she was concerned.

'Had she wanted him to go back to her?—Yes.

'Was she sure that she had been deflowered?—She said yes, and hid her face in her bosom.'

The original text of this examination was

sent to the Grand Duke. Signora Giulia had signed it with a cross.

10

Early in the morning of Thursday, March 15, Master Galletti called at the Gonzaga palace to gather supplementary data. He waited with Donati until the Prince woke up. Joy dominated the palace no less than the little house. Donati, forgetting his temporary lapse, congratulated himself on having shored up everyone's faith.

At seven o'clock the barber came hurrying to usher in Master Galletti. Don Vincenzo, who was in bed, threw off the sheets when the Grand Duke's surgeon came in; 'his person was as straight as a spindle.' Master Galletti 'handled it and remained very satisfied with it.' His report specified that 'the thickness and length are considerable, but not monstrous'; these words brought Florence, Mantua, and the Holy See into line on this much-debated point. When Vinta communicated this decisive anatomical detail to the Grand Duke, he thought how agreeable the comparison with a spindle would be to a reader of the *Capitolo about Spindles* and a lover of proverbs.

In the afternoon, Don Guglielmo's Secretary came to him to say that the Prince wanted to give the young woman 'a present.' Vinta spoke once more of the dowry that the Duke was giving her, on conditions that had now been fulfilled, and reminded him that he could not accept anything on her behalf. When she had been married and dowered by the Grand Duke and Grand Duchess, Don Vincenzo would be free to 'perform a charitable act.' In Venice, it would look like payment for an act of prostitution.

Donati had not finished. He said that the Prince, knowing how much trouble he had caused the knight, would like to recompense him for it in some way. Vinta cut him short immediately. 'He had merely been serving their Most Serene Highnesses, and deserved nothing of the noble Prince except his good will.'

There was nothing left to do but prepare for their departure. Don Vincenzo had arranged to go on March 17; the knight decided to leave Venice on the same day, and informed the Grand Duke accordingly. He would not go through Mantua unless he found instructions to do so awaiting him at Bologna; but he was carrying a copy of the agreement with him in case he should be required to discuss it with Don Guglielmo after all. He would take a different road from the one he had come north by, in order to avoid the traps set by the Farneses and the snares set by the Estes. He thought the return journey would take four days; they would travel by coach, 'for the comfort of the ladies.'

At three o'clock in the morning, the little house was roused by loud knocking. Captain Digni, who no longer had to keep guard on the balcony, went to see who it was. Don Vincenzo's gondolier had brought a note for the knight. 'If Signora Giulia desires H.H.,' wrote Donati, 'your Lordship may bring her to the palace immediately. H.H. is looking forward with great pleasure to seeing her, and will receive her in his own bed, in such a way that she will no doubt be delighted to have come.'

The Secretary added to his signature the description 'Most Excellent Pander' without reflecting that this cap fitted the Florentine, too. Vinta had been styling himself thus for several weeks. Though he considered his rôle no less out of character than Mgr Zibramonti's, he played it as a man of parts, like Urbani in Ferrara.

He was amused by this urgent request at an hour which was not late by Don Vincenzo's standards. He imagined the Prince in the condition he and Master Galletti had recorded. The charger had the bit between its teeth.

Remembering what the young woman had said, he did not doubt that the invitation he brought would be welcome. Contrary to expectations, she was offended and rebuffed him. In vain did he preach obedience, did the matron talk of sensual pleasures, did the surgeon hold out the hope of motherhood, did the captain try to make her afraid. She would yield neither to enticements nor to threats.

The knight had to send Donati a note of apology. He even informed him that Signora Giulia wanted nothing more to do with Don Vincenzo 'either by night or by day'; and he cursed 'the whims of a woman's brain.'

11

When Mgr Abbioso's nurse asked him what he wanted to eat on that Friday before the Passion, the pious Florentine crossed himself. A few hours earlier he had all but committed, permitted, and abetted a grievous sin. The Friday before, he had cooled the Prince's ardour; this Friday, at dawn, he had been his assistant, his accomplice.

This thought reminded him that the Grand Duke and Grand Duchess had enjoined him to respect Holy Week, that the 14th had been St Matilda's Day, and that they were now on the eve of St Longinus' Day, the feast day of Mantua's own patron saint, who carried the Holy Spear and brought the Most Precious Blood. No doubt it was this protector of the Gonzagas who—together with the 'good soul' of Master Guglielmo—had saved the virtue of the congress members this Friday.

Donati went back again to the little house during the morning. He repeated his message of the previous night, but this time as a suppliant. The Prince was bursting. The knight took his stand as a defender of Friday. When Donati begged him to arrange a rendezvous for after midnight, he changed his ground: he was empowered to bring about and supervise an encounter which would lead to an illustrious marriage, not to promote the profligacy of the husband-to-be. That they were exempt from censure did not absolve them *ad infinitum;* the wings of the lion of St Mark were not Cupid's wings; the congress was consummated; virility with virgins had been proved; anything more would be mere lechery. The Most Excellent and Most Catholic Panders would be plain ordinary panders. If it were true, as Don Carlo had said, that the test had taken place 'under the eyes of the whole of Italy,' then it had taken place *a fortiori* under the eyes of the Holy See, which had sanctiond it. Gregory XIII, Cardinal Borromeo, Cardinal Cesi, Cardinal Gonzaga, and the two Medici cardinals could not be indifferent to the Prince's conduct in an adventure for which he had needed a special decree, and not long before an event for which he would need a special dispensation.

He must not pile a Pelion of scandals on an Ossa of indults.

Donati was a skilful advocate for his master's charger. 'After the test, let there be the counter-test,' he said, 'just as there is a dowry and a counterdowry.' Told that Signora Giulia had had a change of heart, he said how preposterous and cruel it was not to make two people happy. Why so much squeamishness, after so many liberties? Had not the knight himself envisaged a return match when he was in doubt about the result of the first? Had he up-rooted the Prince's tree of life the instant it struck root? Had he not left him to make the beast with two backs for several hours? The Consistory had not limited the test to a single act; it therefore permitted a whole series of acts. Moreover exorcisms, prayers, and Franciscan pills had enhanced its religious flavour. Mgr Capilupi, a rigorous moralist, held the entire sojourn in Venice to be blameless.

The knight admitted that he had one other motive for resisting so hard. Having reported to Florence that the test had been a success, he was afraid of the countertest being a failure. Donati, who had guaranteed the one, now guaranteed the other. Everyone at the Gonzaga palace guaranteed it, he added.

At least, said Vinta, he must insist on the girl remaining in the little house. She belonged to the Grand Duke and Grand Duchess, who had entrusted her to his care. He could be sure that all the proceedings at the Congress of Venice were seemly if they took place under a Medici roof.

12

The lovely Giulia shouted for joy when she saw her conqueror. It was five o'clock on the Saturday morning. The Prince had arrived with one of his gentlemen in waiting, Count Tullio Guerriero, and his barber. They changed the sheets, undressed him, helped him on with his night robe, and left him to sink or swim.

It was ten hours before he came out of the room. He was too gallant to vouchsafe any details, but his swaggering air spoke for him. He told the knight that he would be packing his bags that afternoon, and that he too would steer clear of the duchy of Ferrara. He asked Vinta to 'confirm to their Most Serene Highnesses his wish to be their son and servant.' He added that, having nailed to the counter 'the stories spread abroad about his virility,' he hoped soon to see their promises carried out. He said farewell to a weeping Signora Giulia, and left the little house where he had just experienced the varying fortunes of the most important period of his life.

Since the countertest had taken place after all, they might as well record the details. There was no need to study the sheets or the night-clothes. But the towels had been used, and the matron perceived on them 'obvious signs that the noble Prince had worked in earnest.' Signora Giulia, through her tears, murmured that he had 'taken her three times,' that 'the noble Prince's person had been as solid as before,' that there was 'no defect,' and that 'any girl would be pleased with him.'

The knight wrote down her deposition, without examining her. To anticipate any reprimand by the Grand Duke, he described this second visit as unforeseen and added the excuse that there was no harm in making doubly sure.

Before he left, he had a visit from Don Carlo Gonzaga, the gravel in whose bladder had prevented him from accompanying the Prince. He claimed that his joy had half cured him. He was still convinced that Don Vincenzo's lace had been knotted by a diabolical spell, and that they all owed a great deal to Fr Panigarola and Fr Ippolito. And he revealed that to protect the honour of the Gonzagas in the countertest Mgr Capilupi and he had requested the prayers of Mgr Trevisan, Patriarch of Venice.

To this thoroughly Christian devotion, Don Carlo contrasted Mgr Abbioso's frivolous curiosity. The Ambassador had asked the doorkeeper at the Gonzaga palace how many lances the Prince had broken on St Longinus' Day.

Serguidi's congratulations were waiting for Vinta at Bologna:

'Matchless, venerable, and noble knight. Your despatch has restored our spirits, which the previous one had dashed. Praise be to God! Your Lordship has done a deed worthy to go down in history. Their Most Serene Highnesses are very pleased, and they instruct you to come straight back to Florence with your companions. You will have the joy of spending Easter amongst us. The Holy Father has been informed of the successful outcome.'

The Congress of Venice was over.

Part Five

1

On April 11, 1584, the feast day of St Leo the Great, Pope, confessor, and scholar, and the anniversary of the first Consistory on the Prince's person, Gregory XIII, leaning on Cardinals Ferdinando de' Medici and Vastavillani, entered the Sistine Chapel with a Golden Rose in his trembling hand. It was the one he had blessed on *Laetare* Sunday, the day Don Vincenzo had made his début in Venice; and he intended to give it to Donna Eleonora, the Prince's second wife.

Cardinal de' Medici placed the flower in the middle of the altar, then helped the Pope to don the white, gold-embroidered chasuble. Although he was feeble, the Head of the Church wanted to celebrate the office himself, so as to render due homage to the two families which, thanks to the test by congress, had just been united. Cardinal Farnese had sent his apologies, pleading an attack of gout. Mgr Zibramonti (whose Bull for a new erection was at last in the hands of the Affixer of Seals), Mgr Báthory, the King of Poland's nephew, and Mgr de la Corgna, former Nuncio in Florence, had been among the few prelates admitted to the ceremony. The two monks whom the Pope revered had been there, too: Filippo Neri and Felice da Cantalice. They had been continuing their miracles: the founder of the Oratory by restoring to life the son of Marquis Massimo; the Capuchin by curing the Marchioness della Valle of an incurable disease.

Two laymen were there, one on each side of the altar: the Pope's son, Don Giacomo Buoncompagni, Duke of Sora and Arce, Marquis of Vignola, Count of Aquino, and Lord of Arpino, holding the flag of the General of the Holy Roman Church; and Count Segni, Senator of Rome, who was holding the ivory senatorial sceptre for the last time, having been appointed Bishop of Rieti.

In the same chapel, forty years before, Cosimo I had received from Pius V, of blessed memory, the grand ducal crown and the

Golden Rose. It was an exceptional honour for a man, but the Pope had not been able to confer it on Camilla Martelli, the Grand Duke's mistress since his wife's death, nor on his daughter, the Duchess of Bracciano, with whom, as everyone knew, he was carrying on an incestuous liaison. In gratitude, Cosimo I had presented at the offertory a golden chalice, engraved by Benvenuto Cellini, and white vestments embroidered with gold. It was this chalice and these vestments which Gregory XIII was now using.

At the secret Consistory the previous day, he had handed over to Cardinals Gonzaga and Ferdinando de' Medici the dispensations exempting the bride and bridegroom from the prohibition of marriage between related persons. To this he had added another act of grace, for the Princess' sake: an indult granting her, like her stepmother, entry into closed convents. He had earlier absolved from anathema all cardinals who canvassed for votes at, or laid wagers on, the next Conclave—nearly all the Fathers in the purple, in fact.

This mass on April 11, following the Consistory on the 10th, brought together the largest

number of cardinals that Gregory XIII had ever
had around him. Having practised the austeri-
ties of Lent with some rigour, he had so weakened himself that his archiater, Master Atra-
cino, the son of Pope Adrian VI, had reproved
him. His frailness had somewhat exercised
those who meant to have a hand in the succession, and who were no doubt disappointed at
finding themselves so numerous. The art lay in
persuading the Holy Ghost to make a decision
before all his interpreters had arrived in Rome.
That was how Leo X and then Pius V, of blessed
memory, had come to be elected in place of the
future Gregory XIII, who had not managed to
get back from Spain in time. On this occasion
the ambitions of kings as well as of cardinals
had speeded their journeys; only the infirm,
and Cardinal de Guise, were missing. There
was thus a Catholic, apostolic, and Roman
grand finale to the long drama of the Prince's
person. Twenty-eight cardinals had taken part
in the first Consistory; the second was joined
by the nineteen newly created cardinals; fifty-
three, out of a full College of sixty-four, attended the Consistory on April 10; and fifty-

two were present in the Sistine Chapel on April 11.

Mgr Zibramonti, facing the altar, gazed at Michelangelo's fresco of the 'Last Judgment' on the east wall, the nudes in which had been decently obscured by Daniele da Volterra under Paul IV. For the Bishop of Casale they symbolized an affair which he had failed to shroud in decent obscurity.

The sweet voices of the Sistine castrati also reminded him of the Prince's person, of what he had been told about the discussion on the marriage of eunuchs at the first Consistory, and of the Farneses' recent calumnies against Don Vincenzo. The silhouette of Mgr Molari de Fivizzano, the Pope's choirmaster, was cast on Raphael's tapestry of 'The Massacre of the Innocents,' among those of his twenty-four castrati. With a vigorous gesture, he led into the 'Te Deum' for the wife of the Prince whose virility had been sized up so well by Vinta and Galletti.

The Bishop of Casale turned his gaze to the princes of the Church who were solemnly chanting the hymn to gladness instead of reciting the 'De Profundis.' Some of them were on the lookout for signs of faltering in the Pope. They had seen his hand trembling when he lifted the Grand Duke's chalice, as it had trembled while holding the Golden Rose. But their calculations were upset. His high-pitched voice dominated those of the castrati; like the dead or dying whom Fr Filippo Neri and Fr Felice da Cantalice resuscitated, he sang his resurrection.

Mgr Báthory's smooth cheeks caught Mgr Zibramonti's eye. Still a cardinal *in petto,* this prelate was itching to rob the Joyeuse and Santa Fiora families of the title of Prince of the Youth of the Sacred College. He was not far off eighteen, the age at which the Pope had promised to give him this title. No one rejoiced more than he and Don Giacomo at Gregory XIII's access of strength.

In Mgr Zibramonti's view, this 'Te Deum,' behind which so many things were concealed, rewarded most of all those who had laboured in the Lord's vineyard to vindicate his Prince. First of all, the sovereign Pontiff, whose tranquil spirit had set an example to them all; then Cardinal Cesi, his fellow paranymph in these nuptial difficulties; Cardinal Gonzaga, who had kept to the straight path; Cardinal Borromeo, who had woven with his holy hands the thread of the two Consistories; the Medici cardinals, who had wisely promoted the test; Cardinal d'Este, who had stopped Don Guglielmo and Don Alfonso from quarrelling as a result of the Ferrara fiasco; and Cardinal Canano, Bishop of Modena, who had done everything he could.

Cardinal Farnese was absent from this triumph of the Medicis and the Gonzagas, but Mgr Zibramonti associated him with it; after all, it was his surrender that had made the triumph possible. On *Laetare* Sunday he had helped the Pope, blessing the Golden Rose at the church of the Holy Cross of Jerusalem. His name, engraved on the frontispiece of the Church of Jesus, would remain forever in the secret annals of the affair of the Prince's person.

Mgr de la Corgna, who was to take the Rose to Florence, advanced to the middle of the chancel and knelt down. Cardinal de' Medici, the Senior Deacon, handed it to him and pronounced these words: 'Take the Rose which our Holy Father Gregory XIII, Pope by divine providence, has blessed, and which he commands us to entrust to you. This flower symbolizes the gladness of the Church militant and the Church triumphant. It demonstrates the joy of all who believe in Christ; it is the crown of all the Saints. Take it, and, by special order of our Holy Father and Lord in Christ, give it to our beloved daughter, the noble Princess Eleonora de' Medici, so that she may flourish in the world and be scented with numerous virtues, like a rose of Sharon planted beside the waters. In the name of the Father, and of the Son, and of the Holy Ghost. Amen.'

And Gregory XIII, the fifty-two cardinals, the twenty-four castrati, *et tutti quanti* repeated: 'Amen.'

The Bishop of Casale was moved. The Golden Rose seemed to him a symbol, not only of the Church's gladness, but of her wisdom and her glory; it was a purifying veil that she cast over an outwardly unchaste affair.

Mgr Zibramonti thought suddenly of the 'Te Deum' which had been sung by the Benedictine nuns at Parma when Donna Margherita Farnese became Sister Maura Lucenia. Together with the Bishop of Parma and the pious Cardinal Borromeo, he had had a hand in persuading this young girl to make up her mind. And this, in accordance with the designs of providence, was today yielding the more delicate honour that the Holy See was conferring on the Prince of Mantua's new bride. Mgr Zibramonti would have liked to tear off one petal of that rose, to give to the seventeen-year-old nun whom the world had forgotten, but who had not, perhaps, forgotten the world.

Mgr Zibramonti saw another figure in his mind's eye: a virgin that had been carried off from the Ursuline nuns of Florence, to be put at Don Vincenzo's disposal. For her to get a petal from the Golden Rose would have been excessive; but it was only charitable to commend her to the mercy of God.

The Bishop of Casale bowed down in prayer.

2

Donna Eleonora, accompanied by her uncle, the Cardinal and Senior Deacon, and by Don Giovanni de' Medici, her grandfather's bastard, left Florence on April 24. Her retinue consisted of Mgr Pocci, Archbishop of Sienna; Mgr Bandini, Archbishop of Pisa, her steward; the Countess of Carpegna; the knight Vinta, ambassador extraordinary; Arrighi, deputy master surgeon; Ferri, her head page; Fabrice, her dancing master; Dominico, her master tailor; Lorenzo, purveyor of cod; thirty gentlemen in waiting; ten maids of honour; 535 servants; 485 horses; and 190 mules. The Princess carried in her hand the Golden Rose that Mgr de la Corgna had formally presented to her on the 18th, in the church of St Mary of the Flower. When she showed it to the rejoicing crowds, they gave the traditional Florentine cry of 'Balls! Balls!'

Meanwhile, in the chapel of the Ursulines of Piety, the lovely Giulia, made pregnant by the Prince's efforts, was being married to the Roman musician Giuliano. The Grand Duke sent her a dowry of 3,000 crowns; the Cardinal Archbishop sent her his blessing.

It was the Pope who sent his blessing to Don Vincenzo and Donna Eleonora when they were married, at the end of the month, in the palatine church of St Barbara at Mantua. Mgr

Zibramonti had arrived from Rome in time. He brought the Jesuits the Bull for a new erection, and the Prince a gift from the Holy Father: one of the gold medals struck for the wedding of his son. The tailless dragon of his coat-of-arms had grown a new and vigorous tail, under the motto: *Felix praesagium*. The Bishop of Casale and Mgr Capilupi spent the wedding night before the high altar of St Barbara's, where the ampulla of Most Precious Blood had been placed, between the Golden Rose and the medal.

Next morning, after his private mass, Cardinal de' Medici went into the bridal chamber. His niece's embarrassment and Don Vincenzo's air of satisfaction delighted him. The sheets on the bed and the state of the Princess' shift proved that, in Mantua as well as in Venice, 'the noble Prince had worked in earnest.' The Cardinal congratulated the bride and bridegroom, and blessed them. Then he let Master Arrighi verify that the Princess had been deflowered. This was one last formality which the Grand Duke insisted on, and upon which depended the payment of the dowry.

Nothing was entered in a register this time, however.

The 'happy omen' of the pontifical dragon came true, for both the son of the Pope and the son of Don Guglielmo. Don Giacomo Buoncompagni had eleven children. And the man whom the Farneses had accused of impotence had eight—without counting the one begotten in Venice.